# INTERNATIONAL & U.S NAVIGATION RULES

**Including U.S. Aids to Navigation System**

MW00616713

**This amalgamated edition is presented by**
Paradise Cay Publications Inc.
PO Box 29
Arcata, CA 95518-0029

Phone (707) 822-9063
Fax (707) 822-9163
orders@paracay.com
www.paracay.com

**Left Top Photo**

The Coast Guard Cutter Tiger-shark, homeported in Newport, Rhode Island, patrols the Volvo Ocean Race course May 14, 2015. The Coast Guard is responsible for enforcing the safety zone during the week of races.

*Photo by Petty Officer 3rd Class Ross Ruddell*
*U.S. Coast Guard District 1*

**Middle Top Photo**

A 25-foot Response Boat from the Maritime Safety and Security Team San Francisco patrols the safety zone near the Golden Gate Bridge in San Francisco Bay during the 2013 America's Cup race July 7, 2013. Part of the Coast Guard's role in the race is to maintain the flow for commercial vessels entering the Bay.

*Photo by Seaman Erika Lindquist*
*94th Airlift Wing*
*U.S. Coast Guard District 11*

**Right Top Photo**

The Coast Guard Cutter Eagle sails under the Golden Gate Bridge, leading 35 tall ships into San Francisco Bay during the Parade of Sail on July 23, 2008. The Eagle has been in service with the Coast Guard since 1946 following World War II and serves as a training platform for officer candidates to learn leadership, teamwork, seamanship, and navigation skills.

*Photo by Petty Officer 3rd Class Erik Swanson*
*U.S. Coast Guard District 11*

**Bottom Photo**

The M/V Ocean Wind, a 700-foot tanker transits the Mississippi River from Baton Rouge to New Orleans, Louisiana on her way out to sea.
The image captures the constrained traffic which occurs through the River.

*Photo by RADM Sam De Bow, NOAA (Ret.)*
*National Oceanic and Atmospheric Administration*
*National Ocean Service*

**U.S. Department of Homeland Security**

**United States Coast Guard**

Commandant
United States Coast Guard

2703 Martin Luther King Jr Ave, SE,
STOP 7418
Washington, DC 20593-7501
Staff Symbol: CG-NAV-2
Phone: (202) 372-1565
Fax: (202) 475-4173
Email: cgnav@uscg.mil

COMDTCHANGENOTE 16700.4
NVIC 01-16
May 21, 2020

COMMANDANT CHANGE NOTICE 16700.4

Subj: CH-2 TO USE OF ELECTRONIC CHARTS AND PUBLICATIONS IN LIEU OF PAPER CHARTS, MAPS AND PUBLICATIONS, NVIC 01-16, COMDTPUB 16700.4

Ref:  (a) Title 33, Code of Federal Regulations, Parts 83, 161, and 164
      (b) Title 46, Code of Federal Regulations, various parts
      (c) International Convention for Safety of Life at Sea, 1974, and its Protocol of 1988: articles, annexes and certificates, (SOLAS) Chapter V, Regulation 27

1. <u>PURPOSE</u>. This Commandant Change Notice publishes a change to *Use of Electronic Charts and Publications in Lieu of Paper Charts, Maps and Publications*, Navigation and Vessel Inspection Circular number 01-16, 16700.4.

2. <u>ACTION</u>. Officers in Charge, Marine Inspection (OCMI) should bring this Notice to the attention of marine inspectors and the maritime industry within their zones of responsibility. Internet release authorized.

3. <u>DIRECTIVES AFFECTED</u>. With the addition of this Commandant Change Notice, *Use of Electronic Charts and Publications* in lieu of Paper Charts, Maps and Publications, NVIC 01-16 Ch-1, COMDTPUB P16700.4 is updated.

4. <u>DISCLAIMER</u>. This guidance is not a substitute for applicable legal requirements, nor is it itself a rule. It is intended to provide operational guidance for Coast Guard personnel and is not intended to nor does it impose legally binding requirements on any party outside the Coast Guard. It represents the Coast Guard's current thinking on this topic and may assist industry, mariners, the general public, and the Coast Guard, as well as other Federal and state regulators, in applying statutory and regulatory requirements. This Circular prescribes no new requirements for the maritime industry. As such, vessel owners and operators may continue using official paper charts and publications in accordance with References (a) and (b) until the relevant regulations therein are amended.

5. <u>MAJOR CHANGES</u>. In response to recommendations from the Navigation Safety Advisory Council and the public, the Coast Guard updated its policy on electronic carriage of the Inland Navigation Rules and electronic publications in general. This Ch-2 to NVIC 01-16 revises the NVIC, Enclosure (1) and Enclosure (2) to allow electronic editions of the Inland Navigation Rules and Vessel Traffic Service Rules so long as operators are able to display ready reference current electronic editions on their electronic device without internet connectivity by a producing a previously downloaded copy. It also provides a path for mariners to access certain required publications which are not required to be ready reference via web services. Enclosure (2) is further updated to highlight which publications are required by existing regulations to be ready reference and removes the requirement for independent back-ups. Finally, Ch-2 makes non-substantive clarifying changes throughout the NVIC and enclosures.

6. ENVIRONMENTAL ASPECT AND IMPACT CONSIDERATIONS.

a. The development of this instruction and the general policies contained within it have been thoroughly reviewed by the originating office in conjunction with the Office of Environmental Management, Commandant (CG-47). This instruction is categorically excluded under current Department of Homeland Security (DHS) categorical exclusion (CATEX) A3 from further environmental analysis in accordance with the Coast Guard Environmental Planning Policy, COMDTINST 5090.1 and the Environmental Planning (EP) Implementing Procedures (IP).

b. This instruction will not have any of the following: significant cumulative impacts on the human environment; substantial controversy or substantial change to existing environmental conditions; or inconsistencies with any Federal, State, or local laws or administrative determinations relating to the environment. All future specific actions resulting from the general policy in this instruction must be individually evaluated for compliance with the National Environmental Policy Act (NEPA) and Environmental Effects Abroad of Major Federal Actions, Executive Order 12114, Department of Homeland Security (DHS) NEPA policy, Coast Guard Environmental Planning policy, and compliance with all other applicable environmental mandates.

7. DISTRIBUTION. No paper distribution will be made of the Circular. An electronic version will be located on the following Commandant web site: http://www.dco.uscg.mil/Our-Organization/NVIC/

8. PROCEDURE. If maintaining a paper library, remove NVIC 01-16 (CH-1) and Enclosures (1) and (2), and replace them with the updated NVIC 01-16 (CH-2) including updated Enclosures (1) and (2).

9. RECORDS MANAGEMENT CONSIDERATIONS. This Circular has been thoroughly reviewed during the directives clearance process, and it has been determined there are no further records scheduling requirements, in accordance with Federal Records Act, 44 U.S.C. Chapter 31, NARA requirements, and Information and Life Cycle Management Manual, COMDTINST M5212.12 (series). This policy does not have any significant or substantial change to existing records management requirements.

10. FORMS/REPORTS. None.

11. REQUEST FOR CHANGES. Submit recommended changes or questions regarding this guidance to Coast Guard Headquarters, Office of Navigation Systems (CG-NAV-2), using the contact information provided in the above letterhead.

R. V. TIMME
Rear Admiral, U.S. Coast Guard
Assistant Commandant for Prevention Policy

# Record of Changes

## Amendments to the International Navigation Rules (72 COLREGS)

International Navigational Rules Act of 1977
see 91 stat. 308, 33 U.S.C. 1601-1608

International Maritime Organization (IMO) resolutions:
A.464(12), November 19th, 1981
A.626(15), November 19th, 1987
A.678(16), October 19th, 1989
A.736(18), November 4th, 1993
A.910(22), November 29th, 2001
A.1004(25), November 29th, 2007
A.1085(28), December 4th, 2013

## Amendments to the Inland Navigation Rules (33 CFR 83)

Inland Navigational Rules Act of 1980
see 94 stat. 3415, 33 CFR 83

Federal Register documents:
79 FR 37898, July 2nd, 2014
79 FR 68619, November 18th, 2014
80 FR 44274, July 27th, 2015
82 FR 35073, July 18th, 2017
83 FR 3273, January 24th, 2018
84 FR 30870, June 28th, 2019

| RECORD OF CHANGES | | | |
|---|---|---|---|
| CHANGE NUMBER | DATE OF CHANGE | DATE EFFECTIVE | BY WHOM ENTERED |
| | | | |
| | | | |
| | | | |
| | | | |
| | | | |
| | | | |
| | | | |
| | | | |
| | | | |
| | | | |
| | | | |
| | | | |
| | | | |
| | | | |
| | | | |

# Contents

# Introduction

## International Rules

The International Rules in this book were formalized in the Convention on the International Regulations for Preventing Collisions at Sea, 1972, and became effective on July 15, 1977. The Rules (commonly called 72 COLREGS) are part of the Convention, and vessels flying the flags of states ratifying the treaty are bound to the Rules. The United States has ratified this treaty and all United States flag vessels must adhere to these Rules where applicable. President Gerald R. Ford proclaimed 72 COLREGS and the Congress adopted them as the International Navigational Rules Act of 1977.

The 72 COLREGS were developed by the Inter-Governmental Maritime Consultative Organization (IMCO) which in May 1982 was renamed the International Maritime Organization (IMO). In November 1981, IMO's Assembly adopted 55 amendments to the 72 COLREGS which became effective on June 16, 1983. The IMO also adopted 9 more amendments which became effective on June 29, 1989. A single amendment became effective March 19, 1991. In 1993, 8 amendments were adopted by the IMO which entered into force in 1995. The IMO adopted 9 amendments which entered into force November 29, 2003. Lastly, a single amendment was adopted which updated the Distress signals and entered into force on December 1, 2009. The International Rules in this book contain these amendments.

These Rules are applicable on waters outside of established navigational lines of demarcation. The lines are called COLREGS Demarcation Lines and delineate those waters upon which mariners shall comply with the Inland and International Rules. COLREGS Demarcation Lines are contained in this book.

## Inland Regulations

The Inland Rules in this book replace the old Inland Rules, Western Rivers Rules, Great Lakes Rules, their respective pilot rules and interpretive rules, and parts of the Motorboat Act of 1940. Many of the old navigation rules were originally enacted in the 1800's. Occasionally, provisions were added to cope with the increasing complexities of water transportation. Eventually, the navigation rules for United States inland waterways became such a confusing patchwork of requirements that in the 1960's several attempts were made to revise and simplify them. These attempts were not successful.

Following the signing of the Convention on the International Regulations for Preventing Collisions at Sea, 1972, a new effort was made to unify and update the various inland navigation rules. This effort culminated in the enactment of the Inland Navigational Rules Act of 1980. This legislation sets out Rules 1 through 38— the main body of the Rules. The five Annexes were published as regulations. With exception of Annex V to the Inland Rules, the International and Inland Rules and Annexes are very similar in both content and format.

The effective date for the Inland Navigation Rules was December 24, 1981, except for the Great Lakes where the effective date was March 1, 1983.

On May 17, 2010 the US Coast Guard published a Final Rule which placed the Inland Navigational Rules into the Code of Federal Regulations. This move was in accordance with the Coast Guard and Maritime Transportation Act of 2004, which repealed the Inland Navigation Rules as they appeared in United States Code.

The Navigation Rules and Regulations Handbook, formerly produced by the Coast Guard - Office of Navigation Systems, was retired in May 2020. Not all U.S. Navigation Regulations found in Title 33 of the Code of Federal Regulations are contained in this book.

# Amalgamated Navigation Rules

The following is an amalgamation of the International (72 COLREGS) and Inland Navigation Rules, their Annexes, and associated Federal rules and regulations.

We strive to ensure its accuracy. Nonetheless, the National Oceanic and Atmospheric Administration makes no claims or guarantees respecting accuracy and expressly disclaims liability for use of the amalgamation. A hard copy of these rules may be used to meet the requirement in 33 CFR 83.01(g) or Inland Rule 1(g). Introduction

- Text unique to either rule is shown in a text box or within angle brackets.
  - Single-brackets are ‹ International Rules ›.
  - Double-angle brackets with italicized text are « *Inland Rules* ».

- Instances such as "...§§83.xx in / with / of ... this section / subpart / part of this Rule, etc." are redacted with the enumerated Rule(s) or section number. For example, Rule 18(e) states, "... with the Rules of this Part" or "...with the Rules of this Subpart (Rules 4-19) (§§83.04 through 83.19)" is redacted as "...with Rules 4-19".

- Instances such as "paragraph (x)", "section (y)", subsection (1)(z), etc. are redacted with a section symbol, i.e. §(x), §(y) or §(1)(z).

- Dissimilar paragraph or section numbering, and distances are redacted and separated by a dagger symbol, i.e. §(b)‡(ii), [x‡y] meters.

- Annotated text added by the U.S. Coast Guard is denoted by {curly brackets}.

# Legal Citations

## 72 COLREGS

## INLAND RULES

## VESSEL NAVIGATON REGULATIONS

## OPERATIONS OF VESSELS GENERALLY

# Conversion Table

**Conversion of Metric to U.S. Customary/Imperial Units**

| | |
|---|---|
| 1,000 meters .......... 3,280 feet | 6 meters ................. 19.7 feet |
| 500 meters ............ 1,640.4 feet | 5 meters ................. 16.4 feet |
| 200 meters ............ 656.2 feet | 4.5 meters .............. 14.8 feet |
| 150 meters ............ 492.1 feet | 4.0 meters .............. 13.1 feet |
| 100 meters ............ 328.1 feet | 3.5 meters .............. 11.5 feet |
| 75 meters .............. 246.1 feet | 2.5 meters .............. 8.2 feet |
| 60 meters .............. 196.8 feet | 2.0 meters .............. 6.6 feet |
| 50 meters .............. 164.0 feet | 1.5 meters .............. 4.9 feet |
| 25 meters .............. 82.0 feet | 1.0 meters .............. 3.3 feet |
| 20 meters .............. 65.6 feet | 0.9 meters .............. 35.4 inches |
| 12 meters .............. 39.4 feet | 0.6 meters .............. 23.6 inches |
| 10 meters .............. 32.8 feet | 0.5 meters .............. 19.7 inches |
| 8 meters ................ 26.2 feet | 300 millimeters ...... 11.8 inches |
| 7 meters ................ 23.0 feet | 200 millimeters ...... 7.9 inches |

# Part A—General

## Rule 1—Application

### International

(a) These Rules shall apply to all vessels upon the high seas and in all waters connected therewith navigable by seagoing vessels.

(b) Nothing in these Rules shall interfere with the operation of special rules made by an appropriate authority for roadsteads, harbors, rivers, lakes, or inland waterways connected with the high seas and navigable by seagoing vessels. Such special rules shall conform as closely as possible to these Rules.

(c) Nothing in these Rules shall interfere with the operation of any special rules made by the Government of any State with respect to additional station or signal lights, shapes or whistle signals for ships of war and vessels proceeding under convoy, or with respect to additional station or signal lights or shapes for fishing vessels engaged in fishing as a fleet. These additional stations or signal lights, shapes or whistle signals shall, so far as possible, be such that they cannot be mistaken for any light, shape, or signal authorized elsewhere under these Rules.

(d) Traffic separation schemes may be adopted by the Organization for the purpose of these Rules.

(e) Whenever the Government concerned shall have determined that a vessel of special construction or purpose cannot comply fully with the provisions of any of these Rules with respect to number, position, range or arc of visibility of lights or shapes, as well as to the disposition and characteristics of soundsignaling appliances, such vessel shall comply with such other provisions in regard to number, position, range or arc of visibility of lights or shapes, as well as to the disposition and characteristics of sound-signaling appliances, as the Government shall have determined to be the closest possible compliance with these Rules in respect to that vessel.

‡ Submarines may display, as a distinctive means of identification, an intermittent flashing amber (yellow) beacon with a sequence of one flash per second for three (3) seconds followed by a three (3) second off-period (32 CFR 707.7). Other special rules made by the Secretary of the Navy with respect to additional station and signal lights are found in Part 706 of Title 32, Code of Federal Regulations (32 CFR 706).

## Inland

*(a) These rules apply to all vessels upon the inland waters of the United States, and to vessels of the United States on the Canadian waters of the Great Lakes to the extent that there is no conflict with Canadian law. These Rules have preemptive effect over State or local regulation within the same field.*

*(b)(i)These rules constitute special rules made by an appropriate authority within the meaning of Rule 1(b) of the International Regulations for Preventing Collisions at Sea, 1972, including annexes currently in force for the United States ("International Regulations"). (ii) All vessels complying with the construction and equipment requirements of the International Regulations are considered to be in compliance with these Rules.*

*(c) Nothing in these Rules shall interfere with the operation of any special rules made by the Secretary of the Navy with respect to additional station or signal lights and shapes or whistle signals for ships of war and vessels proceeding under convoy, or by the Secretary with respect to additional station or signal lights and shapes for fishing vessels engaged in fishing as a fleet. These additional station or signal lights and shapes or whistle signals shall, so far as possible, be such that they cannot be mistaken for any light, shape or signal authorized elsewhere under these Rules. Notice of such special rules shall be published in the Federal Register and, after the effective date specified in such notice, they shall have effect as if they were a part of these Rules.*

*(d) Traffic separation schemes may be established for the purposes of these Rules. Vessel traffic service regulations may be in effect in certain areas.*

*(e) Whenever the Secretary determines that a vessel or class of vessels of special construction or purpose cannot comply fully with the provisions of any of these Rules with respect to the number, position, range, or arc of visibility of lights or shapes, as well as to the disposition and characteristics of soundsignaling appliances, the vessel shall comply with such other provisions in regard to the number, position, range, or arc of visibility of lights or shapes, as well as to the disposition and characteristics of sound-signaling appliances, as the Secretary shall have determined to be the closest possible compliance with these Rules. The Secretary may issue a certificate of alternative compliance for a vessel or class of vessels specifying the closest possible compliance with these Rules. The Secretary of the Navy shall make these determinations and issue certificates of alternative compliance for vessels of the Navy.*

*(f) The Secretary may accept a certificate of alternative compliance issued by a contracting party to the International Regulations if it determines that the alternative compliance standards of the contracting party are substantially the same as those of the United States.*

*(g) The operator of each self-propelled vessel 12 meters or more in length shall carry, on board and maintain for ready reference, a copy of these Rules.*

## Rule 2—Responsibility

(a) Nothing in these Rules shall exonerate any vessel, or the owner, master, or crew thereof, from the consequences of any neglect to comply with these Rules or of the neglect of any precaution which may be required by the ordinary practice of seamen, or by the special circumstances of the case.

(b) In construing and complying with these Rules due regard shall be had to all dangers of navigation and collision and to any special circumstances, including the limitations of the vessels involved, which may make a departure from these Rules necessary to avoid immediate danger.

## Rule 3—General Definitions

For the purpose of these Rules, except where the context otherwise requires:

(a) The word "vessel" includes every description of watercraft, including non-displacement craft, WIG craft, and seaplanes, used or capable of being used as a means of transportation on water.

(b) The term "power-driven vessel" means any vessel propelled by machinery.

(c) The term "sailing vessel" means any vessel under sail provided that propelling machinery, if fitted, is not being used.

(d) The term "vessel engaged in fishing" means any vessel fishing with nets, lines, trawls, or other fishing apparatus which restrict maneuverability, but does not include a vessel fishing with trolling lines or other fishing apparatus which do not restrict maneuverability.

(e) The term "seaplane" includes any aircraft designed to maneuver on the water.

(f) The term "vessel not under command" means a vessel which through some exceptional circumstance is unable to maneuver as required by these Rules and is therefore unable to keep out of the way of another vessel.

(g) The term "vessel restricted in her ability to maneuver" means a vessel which from the nature of her work is restricted in her ability to maneuver as required by these Rules and is therefore unable to keep out of the way of another vessel. The term "vessels restricted in their ability to maneuver" shall include but not be limited to:
  (i)   A vessel engaged in laying, servicing, or picking up a navigational mark, submarine cable or pipeline;
  (ii)  A vessel engaged in dredging, surveying or underwater operations;
  (iii) A vessel engaged in replenishment or transferring persons, provisions or cargo while underway;
  (iv)  A vessel engaged in the launching or recovery of aircraft;
  (v)   A vessel engaged in mine clearance operations;
  (vi)  A vessel engaged in a towing operation such as severely restricts the towing vessel and her tow in their ability to deviate from their course.

### International

(h) The term "vessel constrained by her draft" means a power-driven vessel which because of her draft in relation to the available depth and width of navigable water is severely restricted in her ability to deviate from the course she is following.

14

(i) The word "underway" means that a vessel is not at anchor, or made fast to the shore, or aground.

(j) The words "length" and "breadth" of a vessel mean her length overall and greatest breadth.

(k) Vessels shall be deemed to be in sight of one another only when one can be observed visually from the other.

(l) The term "restricted visibility" means any condition in which visibility is restricted by fog, mist, falling snow, heavy rainstorms, sandstorms, or any other similar causes.

(m) The term "Wing-In-Ground (WIG)" craft means a multimodal craft which, in its main operational mode, flies in close proximity to the surface by utilizing surface-effect action.

## Inland

*(n) "Western Rivers" means the Mississippi River, its tributaries, South Pass, and South-west Pass, to the navigational demarcation lines {30 CFR 80} dividing the high seas from harbors, rivers and other inland waters of the United States, and the Port Allen-Morgan City Alternate Route, and that part of the Atchafalaya River above its junction with the Port Allen-Morgan City Alternate Route including the Old River and the Red River.*

*(o) "Great Lakes" means the Great Lakes and their connecting tributary waters including the Calumet River as far as the Thomas J. O'Brien Lock and Controlling Waters (between mile 326 and 327), the Chicago River as far as the east side of the Ashland Avenue Bridge (between mile 321 and 322), and the Saint Lawrence River as far east as the lower exit of Saint Lambert Lock.*

*(p) "Secretary" means the Secretary of the Department in which the Coast Guard is operating.*

*(q) "Inland Waters" means the navigable waters of the United States shoreward of the navigational demarcation lines {30 CFR 80} dividing the high seas from harbors, rivers and other inland waters of the United States and the waters of the Great Lakes on the United States side of the International Boundary.*

*(r) "Inland Rules" or "Rules" means these Inland Navigational Rules and the annexes thereto, which govern the conduct of vessels and specify the lights, shapes, and sound signals that apply on inland waters.*

*(s) "International Regulations" means the International Regulations for Preventing Collisions at Sea, 1972, including annexes currently in force for the United States.*

## Inland

**Implementing Rule—33 CFR 89.25 Waters upon which Inland Rules 9(a)(ii), 14(d), and 15(b) apply.**

*Inland Rules 9(a)(ii), 14(d), and 15(b) apply on the Great Lakes, the Western Rivers, and the following specified waters:*

*(a) Tennessee-Tombigbee Waterway.*
*(b) Tombigbee River.*
*(c) Black Warrior River.*
*(d) Alabama River.*
*(e) Coosa River.*
*(f) Mobile River above the Cochrane Bridge at St. Louis Point.*
*(g) Flint River.*
*(h) Chattahoochee River.*
*(i) The Apalachicola River above its confluence with the Jackson River.*

# Part B—Steering and Sailing Rules

## I—Conduct of Vessels in Any Condition of Visibility

### Rule 4—Application

Rules 4 through 10 apply in any condition of visibility.

### Rule 5—Lookout

Every vessel shall at all times maintain a proper look-out by sight and hearing as well as by all available means appropriate in the prevailing circumstances and conditions so as to make a full appraisal of the situation and of the risk of collision.

### Rule 6—Safe Speed

Every vessel shall at all times proceed at a safe speed so that she can take proper and effective action to avoid collision and be stopped within a distance appropriate to the prevailing circumstances and conditions. In determining a safe speed the following factors shall be among those taken into account:

(a) By all vessels:
    (i) The state of visibility;
    (ii) The traffic density including concentrations of fishing vessels or any other vessels;
    (iii) The maneuverability of the vessel with special reference to stopping distance and turning ability in the prevailing conditions;
    (iv) At night, the presence of background light such as from shore lights or from back scatter from her own lights;
    (v) The state of wind, sea and current, and the proximity of navigational hazards;
    (vi) The draft in relation to the available depth of water.

(b) Additionally, by vessels with operational radar:
    (i) The characteristics, efficiency and limitations of the radar equipment;
    (ii) Any constraints imposed by the radar range scale in use;
    (iii) The effect on radar detection of the sea state, weather and other sources of interference;
    (iv) The possibility that small vessels, ice and other floating objects may not be detected by radar at an adequate range;
    (v) The number, location and movement of vessels detected by radar;
    (vi) The more exact assessment of the visibility that may be possible when radar is used to determine the range of vessels or other objects in the vicinity.

# Rule 7—Risk of Collision

(a) Every vessel shall use all available means appropriate to the prevailing circumstances and conditions to determine if risk of collision exists. If there is any doubt such risk shall be deemed to exist.

(b) Proper use shall be made of radar equipment if fitted and operational, including long-range scanning to obtain early warning of risk of collision and radar plotting or equivalent systematic observation of detected objects.

(c) Assumptions shall not be made on the basis of scanty information, especially scanty radar information.

(d) In determining if risk of collision exists the following considerations shall be among those taken into account:

(i) Such risk shall be deemed to exist if the compass bearing of an approaching vessel does not appreciably change.

(ii) Such risk may sometimes exist even when an appreciable bearing change is evident, particularly when approaching a very large vessel or a tow or when approaching a vessel at close range.


# Rule 8—Action to Avoid Collision

(a) Any action taken to avoid collision shall be taken in accordance with Rules 4 through 19 and shall if the circumstances of the case admit, be positive, made in ample time and with due regard to the observance of good seamanship.

(b) Any alteration of course and/or speed to avoid collision shall, if the circumstances of the case admit, be large enough to be readily apparent to another vessel observing visually or by radar; a succession of small alterations of course and/or speed should be avoided.

(c) If there is sufficient sea room, alteration of course alone may be the most effective action to avoid a closequarters situation provided that it is made in good time, is substantial and does not result in another close-quarters situation.

(d) Action taken to avoid collision with another vessel shall be such as to result in passing at a safe distance. The effectiveness of the action shall be carefully checked until the other vessel is finally past and clear.

(e) If necessary to avoid collision or allow more time to assess the situation, a vessel shall slacken her speed or take all way off by stopping or reversing her means of propulsion.

(f) (i) A vessel which, by any of these Rules, is required not to impede the passage or safe passage of another vessel shall, when required by the circumstances of the case, take early action to allow sufficient sea room for the safe passage of the other vessel.

(ii) A vessel required not to impede the passage or safe passage of another vessel is not relieved of this obligation if approaching the other vessel so as to involve risk of collision and shall, when taking action, have full regard to the action which may be required by Rules 4 through 19.

(iii) A vessel, the passage of which is not to be impeded remains fully obliged to comply with Rules 4 through 19 when the two vessels are approaching one another so as to involve risk of collision.

## Rule 9—Narrow Channels

(a) « *(i)* » A vessel proceeding along the course of a narrow channel or fairway shall keep as near to the outer limit of the channel or fairway which lies on her starboard side as is safe and practicable.

### Inland

*(ii) Notwithstanding Rule 9(a)(i) and Rule 14(a), a power-driven vessel operating in narrow channel or fairway on the Great Lakes, Western Rivers, or waters specified by the Secretary, and proceeding downbound with a following current shall have the right-of-way over an upbound vessel, shall propose the manner and place of passage, and shall initiate the maneuvering signals prescribed by Rule 34(a)(i), as appropriate. The vessel proceeding upbound against the current shall hold as necessary to permit safe passing.*

(b) A vessel of less than 20 meters in length or a sailing vessel shall not impede the passage of a vessel ‹ which ›« *that* » can safely navigate only within a narrow channel or fairway.

(c) A vessel engaged in fishing shall not impede the passage of any other vessel navigating within a narrow channel or fairway.

(d) A vessel ‹ shall ›« *must* » not cross a narrow channel or fairway if such crossing impedes the passage of a vessel which can safely navigate only within that channel or fairway. The latter vessel ‹ may ›« *must* » use the signal prescribed in Rule 34(d) if in doubt as to the intention of the crossing vessel.

| International | Inland |
|---|---|
| (e)(i) In a narrow channel or fairway when overtaking can take place only if the vessel to be overtaken has to take action to permit safe passing, the vessel intending to overtake shall indicate her intention by sounding the appropriate signal prescribed in Rule 34(c)(i). The vessel to be overtaken shall, if in agreement, sound the appropriate signal prescribed in Rule 34(c)(ii) and take steps to permit safe passing. If in doubt she may sound the signals prescribed in Rule 34(d). | *(e)(i) In a narrow channel or fairway when overtaking, the power-driven vessel intending to overtake another power-driven vessel shall indicate her intention by sounding the appropriate signal prescribed in Rule 34(c) and take steps to permit safe passing. The powerdriven vessel being overtaken, if in agreement, shall sound the same signal and may, if specifically agreed to, take steps to permit safe passing. If in doubt she shall sound the signal prescribed in Rule 34(d).* |

(e) (ii) This rule does not relieve the overtaking vessel of her obligation under Rule 13.

(f) A vessel nearing a bend or an area of a narrow channel or fairway where other vessels may be obscured by an intervening obstruction shall navigate with particular alertness and caution and shall sound the appropriate signal prescribed in Rule 34(e).

(g) Any vessel shall, if the circumstances of the case admit, avoid anchoring in a narrow channel.

# Rule 10—Traffic Separation Schemes

(a) This Rule applies to traffic separation schemes ‹ adopted by the Organization › and does not relieve any vessel of her obligation under any other rule.

(b) A vessel using a traffic separation scheme shall:
(i) Proceed in the appropriate traffic lane in the general direction of traffic flow for that lane.
(ii) So far as is practicable keep clear of a traffic separation line or separation zone.
(iii) Normally join or leave a traffic lane at the termination of the lane, but when joining or leaving from either side shall do so at as small an angle to the general direction of traffic flow as practicable.

(c) A vessel, shall so far as practicable, avoid crossing traffic lanes but if obliged to do so shall cross on a heading as nearly as practicable at right angles to the general direction of traffic flow.

(d) (i) A vessel shall not use an inshore traffic zone when she can safely use the appropriate traffic lane within the adjacent traffic separation scheme. However, vessels of less than 20 meters in length, sailing vessels and vessels engaged in fishing may use the inshore traffic zone.
(ii) Notwithstanding Rule 10(d)(i), a vessel may use an inshore traffic zone when en route to or from a port, offshore installation or structure, pilot station or any other place situated within the inshore traffic zone, or to avoid immediate danger.

(e) A vessel, other than a crossing vessel or a vessel joining or leaving a lane shall not normally enter a separation zone or cross a separation line except:
(i) in cases of emergency to avoid immediate danger;
(ii) to engage in fishing within a separation zone.

(f) A vessel navigating in areas near the terminations of traffic separation schemes shall do so with particular caution.

(g) A vessel shall so far as practicable avoid anchoring in a traffic separation scheme or in areas near its terminations.

(h) A vessel not using a traffic separating scheme shall avoid it by as wide a margin as is practicable.

(i) A vessel engaged in fishing shall not impede the passage of any vessel following a traffic lane.

(j) A vessel of less than 20 meters in length or a sailing vessel shall not impede the safe passage of a power-driven vessel following a traffic lane.

(k) A vessel restricted in her ability to maneuver when engaged in an operation for the maintenance of safety of navigation in a traffic separation scheme is exempted from complying with this Rule to the extent necessary to carry out the operation.

(l) A vessel restricted in her ability to maneuver when engaged in an operation for the laying, servicing or picking up of a submarine cable, within a traffic separation scheme, is exempted from complying with this Rule to the extent necessary to carry out the operation.

## II—Conduct of Vessels in Sight of One Another

### Rule 11—Application

Rules 11 through 18 apply to vessels in sight of one another.

### Rule 12—Sailing Vessels

(a) When two sailing vessels are approaching one another, so as to involve risk of collision, one of them shall keep out of the way of the other as follows:

(i) when each has the wind on a different side, the vessel which has the wind on the port side shall keep out of the way of the other;

(ii) when both have the wind on the same side, the vessel which is to windward shall keep out of the way of the vessel which is to leeward;

(iii) if a vessel with the wind on the port side sees a vessel to windward and cannot determine with certainty whether the other vessel has the wind on the port or on the starboard side, she shall keep out of the way of the other.

(b) For the purposes of this Rule, the windward side shall be deemed to be the side opposite that on which the mainsail is carried or, in the case of a square-rigged vessel, the side opposite to that on which the largest fore-and-aft sail is carried.

### Rule 13—Overtaking

(a) Notwithstanding anything contained in the Rules 4 through 18, any vessel overtaking any other shall keep out of the way of the vessel being overtaken.

(b) A vessel shall be deemed to be overtaking when coming up with a another vessel from a direction more than 22.5 degrees abaft her beam, that is, in such a position with reference to the vessel she is overtaking, that at night she would be able to see only the sternlight of that vessel but neither of her sidelights.

(c) When a vessel is in any doubt as to whether she is overtaking another, she shall assume that this is the case and act accordingly.

(d) Any subsequent alteration of the bearing between the two vessels shall not make the overtaking vessel a crossing vessel within the meaning of these Rules or relieve her of the duty of keeping clear of the overtaken vessel until she is finally past and clear.

## Rule 14—Head-on Situation

(a) « *Unless otherwise agreed* » when two power-driven vessels are meeting on reciprocal or nearly reciprocal courses so as to involve risk of collision each shall alter her course to starboard so that each shall pass on the port side of the other.

(b) Such a situation shall be deemed to exist when a vessel sees the other ahead or nearly ahead and by night she could see the masthead lights of the other in a line or nearly in a line and/or both sidelights and by day she observes the corresponding aspect of the other vessel.

(c) When a vessel is in any doubt as to whether such a situation exists she shall assume that it does exist and act accordingly.

### Inland

*(d) Notwithstanding Rule 14(a), a power-driven vessel operating on the Great Lakes, Western Rivers, or waters specified by the Secretary, and proceeding downbound with a following current shall have the right-of-way over an upbound vessel, shall propose the manner of passage, and shall initiate the maneuvering signals prescribed by Rule 34(a)(i), as appropriate.*

## Rule 15—Crossing Situation

(a) When two power-driven vessels are crossing so as to involve risk of collision, the vessel which has the other on her own starboard side shall keep out of the way and shall, if the circumstances of the case admit, avoid crossing ahead of the other vessel.

### Inland

*(b) Notwithstanding Rule 15(a), on the Great Lakes, Western Rivers, or water specified by the Secretary, a power-driven vessel crossing a river shall keep out of the way of a power-driven vessel ascending or descending the river.*

## Rule 16—Action by Give-way Vessel

Every vessel which is directed to keep out of the way of another vessel shall, so far as possible, take early and substantial action to keep well clear.

## Rule 17—Action by Stand-on Vessel

(a) (i) Where one of two vessels is to keep out of the way, the other shall keep her course and speed.

(ii) The latter vessel may, however, take action to avoid collision by her maneuver alone, as soon as it becomes apparent to her that the vessel required to keep out of the way is not taking appropriate action in compliance with these Rules.

(b) When, from any cause, the vessel required to keep her course and speed finds herself so close that collision cannot be avoided by the action of the giveway vessel alone, she shall take such action as will best aid to avoid collision.

(c) A power-driven vessel which takes action in a crossing situation in accordance with Rule 17(a)(ii) to avoid collision with another power-driven vessel shall, if the circumstances of the case admit, not alter course to port for a vessel on her own port side.

(d) This Rule does not relieve the give-way vessel of her obligation to keep out of the way.


## Rule 18—Responsibilities Between Vessel

Except where Rules 9, 10, and 13 otherwise require:

(a) A power-driven vessel underway shall keep out of the way of:
    (i) a vessel not under command;
    (ii) a vessel restricted in her ability to maneuver;
    (iii) a vessel engaged in fishing;
    (iv) a sailing vessel.

(b) A sailing vessel underway shall keep out of the way of:
    (i) a vessel not under command;
    (ii) a vessel restricted in her ability to maneuver;
    (iii) a vessel engaged in fishing.

(c) A vessel engaged in fishing when underway shall, so far as possible, keep out of the way of:
    (i) a vessel not under command;
    (ii) a vessel restricted in her ability to maneuver.

### International

*(d) (i) Any vessel other than a vessel not under command or a vessel restricted in her ability to maneuver shall, if the circumstances of the case admit, avoid impeding the safe passage of a vessel constrained by her draft, exhibiting the signals in Rule 28.*

*(ii) A vessel constrained by her draft shall navigate with particular caution having full regard to her special condition.*

(e) A seaplane on the water shall, in general, keep well clear of all vessels and avoid impeding their navigation. In circumstances, however, where risk of collision exists, she shall comply with Rules 4 through 19.

(f) (i) A WIG craft shall, when taking off, landing and in flight near the surface, keep well clear of all other vessels and avoid impeding their navigation;

(ii) a WIG craft operating on the water surface shall comply with Rules 4 through 19 as a power-driven vessel.

# III—Conduct of Vessels in Restricted Visibility

## Rule 19—Conduct of Vessels in Restricted Visibility

(a) This Rule applies to vessels not in sight of one another when navigating in or near an area of restricted visibility.

(b) Every vessel shall proceed at a safe speed adapted to the prevailing circumstances and conditions of restricted visibility. A power-driven vessel shall have her engines ready for immediate maneuver.

(c) Every vessel shall have due regard to the prevailing circumstances and conditions of restricted visibility when complying with Rules 4 through 10.

(d) A vessel which detects by radar alone the presence of another vessel shall determine if a closequarters situation is developing and/or risk of collision exists. If so, she shall take avoiding action in ample time, provided that when such action consists of an alteration in course, so far as possible the following shall be avoided:
   (i) An alteration of course to port for a vessel forward of the beam, other than for a vessel being overtaken;
   (ii) An alteration of course toward a vessel abeam or abaft the beam.

(e) Except where it has been determined that a risk of collision does not exist, every vessel which hears apparently forward of her beam the fog signal of another vessel, or which cannot avoid a close-quarters situation with another vessel forward of her beam, shall reduce her speed to be the minimum at which she can be kept on her course. She shall if necessary take all her way off and in any event navigate with extreme caution until danger of collision is over.

# Part C—Lights and Shapes

## Rule 20—Application

(a) Rules 20 through 31 shall be complied with in all weathers.

(b) The Rules concerning lights shall be complied with from sunset to sunrise, and during such times no other lights shall be exhibited, except such lights which cannot be mistaken for the lights specified in these Rules or do not impair their visibility or distinctive character, or interfere with the keeping of a proper look-out.

(c) The lights prescribed by these Rules shall, if carried, also be exhibited from sunrise to sunset in restricted visibility and may be exhibited in all other circumstances when it is deemed necessary.

(d) The Rules concerning shapes shall be complied with by day.

(e) The lights and shapes specified in these Rules shall comply with the provisions of Annex I of these Rules.

### Inland

*(f) A vessel's navigation lights and shapes may be lowered if necessary to pass under a bridge.*

## Rule 21—Definitions

(a) "Masthead light" means a white light placed over the fore and aft centerline of the vessel showing an unbroken light over an arc of the horizon of 225° and so fixed as to show the light from right ahead to 22.5° abaft the beam on either side of the vessel « *except that on a vessel of less than 12 meters in length the masthead light shall be placed as nearly as practicable to the fore and aft centerline of the vessel* ».

(b) "Sidelights" means a green light on the starboard side and a red light on the port side each showing an unbroken light over an arc of the horizon of 112.5° and so fixed as to show the light from right ahead to 22.5° abaft the beam on its respective side.

In a vessel of less than 20 meters in length the sidelights may be combined in one lantern carried on the fore and aft centerline of the vessel « , *except that on a vessel of less than 12 meters in length the sidelights when combined in one lantern shall be placed as nearly as practicable to the fore and aft centerline of the vessel* ».

(c) "Sternlight" means a white light placed as nearly as practicable at the stern showing an unbroken light over an arc of the horizon of 135° and so fixed as to show the light 67.5° from right aft on each side of the vessel.

(d) "Towing light" means a yellow light having the same characteristics as the "sternlight" defined in Rule 21(c).

(e) "All-round light" means a light showing an unbroken light over an arc of the horizon of 360°.

(f) "Flashing light" means a light flashing at regular intervals at a frequency of 120 flashes or more per minute.

## Inland

*(g) "Special flashing light" means a yellow light flashing at regular intervals at a frequency of 50 to 70 flashes per minute, placed as far forward and as nearly as practicable on the fore and aft centerline of the tow and showing an unbroken light over an arc of the horizon of not less than 180 degrees nor more than 225 degrees and so fixed as to show the light from right ahead to abeam and no more than 22.5 degrees abaft the beam on either side of the vessel.*

## Inland—Annex V Pilot Rules 33 CFR 88

**§88.05 Law enforcement vessels. {Flashing blue light}**
*(a) Law enforcement vessels may display a flashing blue light when engaged in direct law enforcement or public safety activities. This light must be located so that it does not interfere with the visibility of the vessel's navigation lights. (b) The blue light described in this section may be displayed by law enforcement vessels of the United States and the States and their political subdivisions.*

**§88.07 Public safety activities. {Alternating flashing red and yellow light}**
*(a) Vessels engaged in government sanctioned public safety activities, and commercial vessels perform-ing similar functions, may display an alternately flashing red and yellow light signal. This identification light signal must be located so that it does not interfere with the visibility of the vessel's navigation lights. The identification light signal may be used only as an identification signal and conveys no special privilege. Vessels using the identification light signal during public safety activities must abide by the Inland Naviga-tion Rules, and must not presume that the light or the exigency gives them precedence or right of way. (b) Public safety activities include but are not limited to patrolling marine parades, regattas, or special water celebrations; traffic control; salvage; firefighting; medical assistance; assisting disabled vessels; and search and rescue.*

## Rule 22—Visibility of Lights

The lights prescribed in these Rules (Subpart C) shall have an intensity as specified in Annex I to these Rules (33 CFR part 84), so as to be visible at the following minimum ranges:

(a) In a vessel of 50 meters or more in length:
    (i) a masthead light, 6 miles;
    (ii) a sidelight, 3 miles;
    (iii) a sternlight, 3 miles;
    (iv) a towing light, 3 miles;
    (v) a white, red, green or yellow all-round light, 3 miles; and
    « (vi) a special flashing light, 2 miles. »

(b) In a vessel of 12 meters or more in length but less than 50 meters in length:
    (i) a masthead light, 5 miles; except that where the length of the vessel is less than 20 meters, 3 miles;
    (ii) a sidelight, 2 miles;
    (iii) a sternlight, 2 miles;
    (iv) a towing light, 2 miles;
    (v) a white, red, green or yellow all-round light, 2 miles; and
    « (vi) a special flashing light, 2 miles. »

(c) In a vessel of less than 12 meters in length:
    (i) a masthead light, 2 miles;
    (ii) a sidelight, 1 mile;
    (iii) a sternlight, 2 miles;
    (iv) A towing light, 2 miles;
    (v) a white, red, green or yellow all-round light, 2 miles; and
    « (vi) a special flashing light, 2 miles. »

(d) In an inconspicuous, partly submerged vessel or objects being towed:
    (i) A white all-round light, 3 miles.

# Rule 23—Power-driven Vessels Underway

(a) A power-driven vessel underway shall exhibit:

(i) a masthead light forward;

(ii) a second masthead light abaft of and higher than the forward one; except that a vessel of less than 50 meters in length shall not be obliged to exhibit such a light but may do so;

(iii) sidelights; and

(iv) a sternlight.

Power-driven Vessel Underway
50 meters or greater in length

Power-driven Vessel Underway
Less than 50 meters in length

(b) An air-cushion vessel when operating in non-displacement mode shall, in addition to the lights prescribed in Rule 23(a), exhibit an all-round flashing yellow light «, *where it can best be seen* ».

Air-cushion vessel when operating in the
non-displacement mode—
Vessels less than 50 meters in length

Air-cushion vessel when operating in the
displacement mode—
Vessels less than 50 meters in length

(c) A WIG craft only when taking off, landing and in flight near the surface shall, in addition to the lights prescribed in Rule 23(a), exhibit a high intensity allround flashing red light.

# Rule 23—Power-driven Vessels Underway CONTINUED

(d) (i) A power-driven vessel of less than 12 meters in length may in lieu of the lights prescribed in Rule 23(a) exhibit an all-round white light and sidelights.

Power-driven Vessel.  Less than 12 meters in length

## International

(ii) a power-driven vessel of less than 7 meters in length whose maximum speed does not exceed 7 knots may in lieu of the lights prescribed in Rule 23(a) exhibit an all-round white light and shall, if practicable, also exhibit sidelights.

Power-driven Vessel. Less than 7 meters in length

(iii) the masthead light or all-round white light on a power-driven vessel of less than 12 metres in length may be displaced from the fore and aft centre line of the vessel if centreline fitting is not practicable, provided that the sidelights are combined in one lantern which shall be carried on the fore and aft centre line of the vessel or located as nearly as practicable in the same fore and aft line as the masthead light or the all-round white light.

## Inland

(e) *A power-driven vessel when operating on the Great Lakes may carry an allround white light in lieu of the second masthead light and sternlight prescribed in Rule 23(a). The light shall be carried in the position of the second masthead light and be visible at the same minimum range.*

Power-driven Vessel on the Great Lakes

# Rule 24—Towing and Pushing

(a) A power-driven vessel when towing astern shall exhibit:

(i) instead of the light prescribed in Rule 23(a)(i) or 23(a)(ii), two masthead lights in a vertical line. When the length of the tow, measuring from the stern of the towing vessel to the after end of the tow, exceeds 200 meters, three such lights in a vertical line;

(ii) sidelights;

(iii) a sternlight;

(iv) a towing light in a vertical line above the sternlight; and

(v) when the length of the tow exceeds 200 meters, a diamond shape where it can best be seen.

Power-driven Vessel Towing Astern
Towing vessel less than 50 meters in length;
length of tow exceeds 200 meters

Power-driven Vessel Towing Astern Towing
vessel less than 50 meters in length; length of
tow 200 meters or less

(b) When a pushing vessel and a vessel being pushed ahead are rigidly connected in a composite unit they shall be regarded as a power-driven vessel and exhibit the lights prescribed in Rule 23.

Composite Unit Underway.
Same for inland.

Composite unit underway - less than
50 meters in length.
Same for international.

# Rule 24—Towing and Pushing CONTINUED

## International

**Interpretive Rule—33 CFR 82.3 Pushing vessel and vessel being pushed: Composite unit.**

Rule 24(b) of the 72 COLREGS states that when a pushing vessel and a vessel being pushed ahead are rigidly connected in a composite unit, they are regarded as a power-driven vessel and must exhibit the lights under Rule 23. A "composite unit" is interpreted to be a pushing vessel that is rigidly connected by mechanical means to a vessel being pushed so they react to sea and swell as one vessel. "Mechanical means" does not include the following:

(a) Lines.
(b) Hawsers.
(c) Wires.
(d) Chains.

## Inland

*Interpretive Rule—33 CFR 90.3 Pushing vessel and vessel being pushed: Composite unit.*

*Rule 24(b) of the Inland Rules states that when a pushing vessel and a vessel being pushed ahead are rigidly connected in a composite unit, they are regarded as a power-driven vessel and must exhibit the lights prescribed in Rule 23. A "composite unit" is interpreted to be the combination of a pushing vessel and a vessel being push ahead that are rigidly connected by mechanical means so they react to sea and swell as one vessel. Mechanical means does not include lines, wires, hawsers, or chains.*

(c) A power-driven vessel when pushing ahead or towing alongside, except ‹ in the case of a composite unit ›‹‹ *as required by Rules 24(b) and (i)* ››, shall exhibit:
(i) instead of the light prescribed in Rule 23(a)(i) or 23(a)(ii), two masthead lights in a vertical line;
(ii) sidelights; and
(iii) ‹ a sternlight ›‹‹ *two towing lights in a vertical line* ››.

(d) A power-driven vessel to which paragraphs (a) or (c) of this Rule applies shall also comply with Rule 23 ‹‹ *(a)(i) and* ›› (a)(ii).

**Power-driven Vessel Towing Astern**
Length of tow 200 meters or less; the after masthead light is optional for vessels less than 50 meters in length

**Power-driven Vessel Towing Astern**
When masthead lights for towing or pushing are exhibited aft, a forward masthead light is required

(e) A vessel or object being towed, other than those ‹ mentioned ›‹‹ *referred* ›› in Rule 24(g), shall exhibit:

(i) sidelights;

(ii) a sternlight;

(iii) when the length of the tow exceeds 200 meters, a diamond shape where it can best be seen.

**Vessel Being Towed**
**Length of tow 200 meters or less**

**Vessel or Object Being Towed**
**Length of tow exceeds 200 meters**

(f) Provided that any number of vessels being towed alongside or pushed in a group shall be lighted as one vessel ‹‹ *except as provided in Rule 24(f)(iii)* ››.

(i) a vessel being pushed ahead, not being part of a composite unit, shall exhibit at the forward end, sidelights, and ‹‹ *a special flashing light* ››;

(ii) a vessel being towed alongside shall exhibit a sternlight and at the forward end, sidelights, and ‹‹ *a special flashing light* ››;

## International

**Vessel Being Pushed Ahead**
**Not being part of a composite unit**

**Vessel Being Towed Alongside**

## Inland

**Vessel Being Pushed Ahead**
**Not being part of a composite unit**

**Vessel Being Towed Alongside**

# Rule 24—Towing and Pushing CONTINUED

## Inland

> *(iii) when vessels are towed alongside on both sides of the towing vessel a sternlight shall be exhibited on the stern of the outboard vessel on each side of the towing vessel, and a single set of sidelights as far forward and as far outboard as is practicable, and a single special flashing light;*

(g) An inconspicuous, partly submerged vessel or object, or combination of such vessels or objects being towed, shall exhibit:
   (i) if it is less than 25 meters in breadth, one all-round white light at or near the forward end and one at or near the after end except that dracones need not exhibit a light at or near ‹ the forward ›‹‹ *each* ›› end.

| International | Inland |
|---|---|
| (ii) if it is 25 meters or more in breadth, two additional all-round white lights at or near the extremities of its breadth; | *(ii) if it is 25 meters or more in breadth, four all-round white lights to mark its length and breadth;* |

(iii) if it exceeds 100 meters in length, additional allround white lights between the lights prescribed in Rule 24(g)(i) ‹‹ *and (ii)* ›› and so that the distance between the lights shall not exceed 100 meters. ‹‹ *Provided that any vessels or objects being towed alongside each other shall be lighted as one vessel or object* ››.
(iv) a diamond shape at or near the aftermost extremity of the last vessel or object being towed; and ‹ if the length of the tow exceeds 200 meters an additional diamond shape where it can best be seen and located as far forward as is practicable. ›

## Inland

> *(v) the towing vessel may direct a searchlight in the direction of the tow to indicate its presence to an approaching vessel.*

(h) Where from any sufficient cause it is impracticable for a vessel or object being towed to exhibit the lights or shapes prescribed in Rule 24(e) or (g), all possible measures shall be taken to light the vessel or object towed or at least to indicate the presence of ‹ such ›‹‹ *the unlighted* ›› vessel or object.

| International | Inland |
|---|---|
| **Interpretive Rule—33 CFR 82.7 Sidelights for unmanned barges.** | ***Interpretive Rule—33 CFR 90.7 Sidelights for unmanned barges.*** |
| An unmanned barge being towed may use the exception of COLREGS Rule 24(h). However, this exception only applies to the vertical sector requirements. | *An unmanned barge being towed may use the exception of COLREGS Rule 24(h). However, this exception only applies to the vertical sector requirements for sidelights.* |

(i) Where from any sufficient cause it is impracticable for a vessel not normally engaged in towing operations to display the lights prescribed by paragraph (a), (c), « *or (j)* » of this Rule, such vessel shall not be required to exhibit those lights when engaged in towing another vessel in distress or otherwise in need of assistance. All possible measures shall be taken to indicate the nature of the relationship between the towing vessel and the vessel being towed ‹ as authorized by Rule 36, in particular by illuminating the towline ›« *and the vessel being assisted. The searchlight authorized by Rule 36 may be used to illuminate the tow* ».

## Inland

*(j) Notwithstanding paragraph (c) of this Rule, on the Western Rivers (except below the Huey P. Long Bridge at mile 106.1 Above Head of Passes on the Mississippi River) and on waters specified by the Secretary, a power-driven vessel when pushing ahead or towing alongside, except as paragraph (b) of this Rule applies, shall exhibit: (i) sidelights; and (ii) two towing lights in a vertical line.*

## Inland

### Implementing Rule—33 CFR 89.27 Waters upon which Inland Rule 24(j) applies.

*(a) Inland Rule 24(j) applies on the Western Rivers and the specified waters listed in §89.25 (a) through (i).*

*(b) Inland Rule 24(j) applies on the Gulf Intracoastal Waterway from St. Marks, Florida, to the Rio Grande, Texas, including the Morgan City-Port Allen Alternate Route and the Galveston-Freeport Cutoff, except that a power-driven vessel pushing ahead or towing alongside shall exhibit the lights required by Inland Rule 24(c), while transiting within the following areas:*

*(1) St. Andrews Bay from the Hathaway Fixed Bridge at Mile 284.6 East of Harvey Locks (EHL) to the DuPont Fixed Bridge at Mile 295.4 EHL.*

*(2) Pensacola Bay, Santa Rosa Sound and Big Lagoon from the Light "10" off of Trout Point at Mile 176.9 EHL to the Pensacola Fixed Bridge at Mile 189.1 EHL.*

*(3) Mobile Bay and Bon Secour Bay from the Dauphin Island Causeway Fixed Bridge at Mile 127.7 EHL to Little Point Clear at Mile 140 EHL.*

*(4) Mississippi Sound from Grand Island Waterway Light "1" at Mile 53.8 EHL to Light "40" off the West Point of Dauphin Island at Mile 118.7 EHL.*

*(5) The Mississippi River at New Orleans, Mississippi River-Gulf Outlet Canal and the Inner Harbor Navigation Canal from the junction of the Harvey Canal and the Algiers Alternate Route at Mile 6.5 West of Harvey Locks (WHL) to the Michoud Canal at Mile 18 EHL.*

*(6) The Calcasieu River from the Calcasieu Lock at Mile 238.6 WHL to the Ellender Lift Bridge at Mile 243.6 WHL.*

*(7) The Sabine Neches Canal from mile 262.5 WHL to mile 291.5 WHL.*

*(8) Bolivar Roads from the Bolivar Assembling Basin at Mile 346 WHL to the Galveston Causeway Bridge at Mile 357.3 WHL.*

*(9) Freeport Harbor from Surfside Beach Fixed Bridge at Mile 393.8 WHL to the Bryan Beach Pontoon Bridge at Mile 397.6 WHL.*

*(10) Matagorda Ship Channel area of Matagorda Bay from Range "K" Front Light at Mile 468.7 WHL to the Port O'Connor Jetty at Mile 472.2 WHL.*

*(11) Corpus Christi Bay from Redfish Bay Day Beacon "55" at Mile 537.4 WHL when in the Gulf Intracoastal Waterway main route or from the north end of Lydia Ann Island Mile 531.1A when in the Gulf Intracoastal Waterway Alternate Route to Corpus Christi Bay LT 76 at Mile 543.7 WHL.*

*(12) Port Isabel and Brownsville Ship Channel south of the Padre Island Causeway Fixed Bridge at Mile 665.1 WHL.*

# Rule 25—Sailing Vessels Underway and Vessels Under Oars

(a) A sailing vessel underway shall exhibit:
    (i) sidelight;
    (ii) a sternlight.

(b) In a sailing vessel of less than 20 meters in length the lights prescribed in Rule 25(a) may be combined in one lantern carried at or near the top of the mast where it can best be seen.

(c) A sailing vessel underway may, in addition to the lights prescribed in Rule 25(a), exhibit at or near the top of the mast, where they can best be seen, two allround lights in a vertical line, the upper being red and the lower green, but these lights shall not be exhibited in conjunction with the combined lantern permitted by Rule 25(b).

(a) Sailing Vessel
Underway

(b) Sailing Vessel
Underway
Less than 20 meters
in length

(d) (i) A sailing vessel of less than 7 meter in length shall, if practicable, exhibit the lights prescribed in Rule 25(a) or (b), but if she does not, she shall « exhibit an all around white light or » have ready at hand an electric torch or lighted lantern showing a white light which shall be exhibited in sufficient time to prevent collision.

    (ii) A vessel under oars may exhibit the lights prescribed in this rule for sailing vessels, but if she does not, she shall « exhibit an all around white light or » have ready at hand an electric torch or lighted lantern showing a white light which shall be exhibited in sufficient time to prevent collision.

(c) Sailing Vessel
Underway

(e) A vessel proceeding under sail when also being propelled by machinery shall exhibit forward where it can best be seen a conical shape, apex downwards. « A vessel of less than 12 meters in length is not required to exhibit this shape, but may do so. »

(d i) Sailing Vessel
Underway
Less than 7 meters
in length

(d ii) Vessel Under
Oars

# Rule 26—Fishing Vessels

(a) A vessel engaged in fishing, whether underway or at anchor, shall exhibit only the lights and shapes prescribed in this Rule.

(b) A vessel when engaged in trawling, by which is meant the dragging through the water of a dredge net or other apparatus used as a fishing appliance, shall exhibit:

(i) two all-round lights in a vertical line, the upper being green and the lower white, or a shape consisting of two cones with their apexes together in a vertical line one above the other;

(ii) a masthead light abaft of and higher than the all-round green light; a vessel of less than 50 meters in length shall not be obliged to exhibit such a light but may do so;

(iii) when making way through the water, in addition to the lights prescribed in this paragraph, sidelights and a sternlight.

**Vessel Engaged in Trawling**
**Not making way**

**Vessel Engaged in Trawling**
**Not making way; less than 50 meters in length**

**Vessel Engaged in Trawling**
**Making way**

**Vessel Engaged in Trawling**
**Making way; less than 50 meters in length**

# Rule 26—Fishing Vessels CONTINUED

(c) A vessel engaged in fishing, other than trawling, shall exhibit:

(i) two all-round lights in a vertical line, the upper being red and the lower white, or a shape consisting of two cones with their apexes together in a vertical line one above the other;

(ii) when there is outlying gear extending more than 150 meters horizontally from the vessel, an all-round white light or a cone apex upwards in the direction of the gear;

(iii) when making way through the water, in addition to the lights prescribed in this paragraph, sidelights and a sternlight.

**Vessel Engaged in Fishing Other Than Trawling. Making way**

**Vessel Engaged in Fishing Other Than Trawling. Not making way**

When there is outlying gear extending more than 150 meters horizontally from the vessel, an allround white light or a cone apex upwards in the direction of the gear.

## International

(d) The additional signals described in Annex II to these Regulations apply to a vessel engaged in fishing in close proximity to other vessels engaged in fishing.

(e) A vessel ‹when› not engaged in fishing shall not exhibit the lights or shapes prescribed in this Rule, but only those prescribed for a vessel of her length.

*« (f) Additional signals for fishing vessels in close proximity. »* {Same as International Rules Annex II}

1‡(i) The lights mentioned herein shall ‹ ,if exhibited in pursuance of Rule 26(d), › be placed where they can best be seen. They shall be at least 0.9 meters apart but at a lower level than lights prescribed in Rule 26. ‹ (b)(i) and (c)(i) › The lights shall be visible all round the horizon at a distance of at least 1 mile but at a lesser distance from the lights prescribed by ‹ these Rules › *« Rule 26(a)-(c) for fishing vessels. »*

2‡(ii) Signals for trawlers.

(a)‡(1) Vessels ‹ of 20 meters or more in length › when engaged in trawling, whether using demersal or pelagic gear, ‹ shall ›« *may* » exhibit:

(i)‡(A) when shooting their nets: two white lights in a vertical line;

(ii)‡(B) when hauling their nets: one white light over one red light in a vertical line;

(iii)‡(C) when the net has come fast upon an obstruction: two red lights in a vertical line.

(b)‡(2) ‹ A ›« *Each* » vessel ‹ of 20 meters or more in length › engaged in pair trawling ‹ shall ›« *may* » exhibit:

(i)‡(A) by night, a searchlight directed forward and in the direction of the other vessel of the pair;

(ii)‡(B) when shooting or hauling their nets or when their nets have come fast upon an obstruction, the lights prescribed in Rule 26(f)(2)(a)‡(f)(ii)(1).

3‡(iii) Signals for purse seiners.

(a)‡(1) Vessels engaged in fishing with purse seine gear may exhibit two yellow lights in a vertical line. These lights shall flash alternately every second and with equal light and occultation duration. These lights may be exhibited only when the vessel is hampered by its fishing gear.

# Rule 27—Vessels Not Under Command or Restricted in Their Ability to Maneuver

(a) A vessel not under command shall exhibit:

(i) two all-round red lights in a vertical line where they can best be seen;

(ii) two balls or similar shapes in a vertical line where they can best be seen;

(iii) when making way through the water, in addition to the lights prescribed in this paragraph, sidelights and a sternlight.

Vessel Not Under Command  
Not making way

Vessel Not Under Command  
Making way

# Rule 27—Vessels Not Under Command or Restricted in Their Ability to Maneuver CONTINUED

(b) A vessel restricted in her ability to maneuver, except a vessel engaged in mineclearance operations, shall exhibit:

(i) three all-round lights in a vertical line where they can best be seen. The highest and lowest of these lights shall be red and the middle light shall be white;

(ii) three shapes in a vertical line where they can best be seen. The highest and lowest of these shapes shall be balls and the middle one a diamond;

(iii) when making way through the water, a masthead light(s), sidelights and a sternlight in addition to the lights prescribed in Rule 27(b)(i); (iv) when at anchor, in addition to the lights or shapes prescribed in Rule 27(b)(i) and (ii), the light, lights, or shapes prescribed in Rule 30.

Vessel Restricted in Her Ability to Maneuver—
Making way; less than 50 meters in length

Vessel Restricted in Her Ability to Maneuver—
At anchor; less than 50 meters in length

(c) A power-driven vessel engaged in a towing operation such as severely restricts the towing vessel and her tow in their ability to deviate from their course shall, in addition to the lights or shape prescribed in Rule 27(b) (i) and (ii), exhibit the lights or shape prescribed in Rule 24.

Vessel engaged in towing operation which severely restricts
towing vessel and her tow in their ability to deviate from
their course
Length of tow does not exceed 200 meters; towing vessel
less than 50 meters in length

(d) A vessel engaged in dredging or underwater operations, when restricted in her ability to maneuver, shall exhibit the lights and shapes prescribed in Rules 27(b)(i), (ii) and (iii) and shall in addition when an obstruction exists, exhibit:

(i) two all-round red lights or two balls in a vertical line to indicate the side on which the obstruction exists;

(ii) two all-round green lights or two diamonds in a vertical line to indicate the side on which another vessel may pass; and

(iii) when at anchor, the lights or shapes prescribed in this paragraph instead of the lights or shapes prescribed in Rule 30.

Vessel engaged in dredging or underwater operations when restricted in ability to maneuver. Making way with an obstruction on the starboard side

Vessel engaged in dredging or underwater operations when restricted in ability to maneuver. Not making way with an obstruction on the starboard side

## Inland

*(iv) Dredge pipelines that are floating or supported on trestles shall display the following lights at night and in periods of restricted visibility.*

*(1) One row of yellow lights. The lights must be:*
  *(A) flashing 50 to 70 times per minute,*
  *(B) visible all round the horizon,*
  *(C) visible for at least 2 miles,*
  *(D) not less than 1 and not more than 3.5 meters above the water,*
  *(E) approximately equally spaced, and*
  *(F) not more than 10 meters apart where the pipeline crosses a navigable channel. Where the pipeline does not cross a navigable channel the lights must be sufficient in number to clearly show the pipeline's length and course.*

*(2) Two red lights at each end of the pipeline, including the ends in a channel where the pipeline is separated to allow vessels to pass (whether open or closed). The lights must be:*
  *(A) visible all round the horizon, and*
  *(B) visible for at least 2 miles, and*
  *(C) one meter apart in a vertical line with the lower light at the same height above the water as the flashing yellow light.*

## Rule 27—Vessels Not Under Command or Restricted in Their Ability to Maneuver CONTINUED

(e) Whenever the size of a vessel engaged in diving operations makes it impracticable to exhibit all lights and shapes prescribed in Rule 27(d), the following shall be exhibited:

(i) Three all-round lights in a vertical line where they can best be seen. The highest and lowest of these lights shall be red and the middle light shall be white;

(ii) a rigid replica of the International Code flag "A" not less than 1 meter in height. Measures shall be taken to ensure its all-round visibility.

Small vessel engaged in diving operations

(f) A vessel engaged in mine clearance operations shall, in addition to the lights prescribed for a power-driven vessel in Rule 23 or to the lights or shape prescribed for a vessel at anchor in Rule 30 as appropriate, exhibit three all-round green lights or three balls. One of these lights or shapes shall be exhibited near the foremast head and one at each end of the fore yard. These lights or shapes indicate that it is dangerous for another vessel to approach within 1000 meters of the mineclearance vessel.

Vessel engaged in mineclearance operations
Vessel less than 50 meters in length

Vessel engaged in mineclearance operations
Vessel 50 meters or greater in length

(g) Vessels of less than 12 meters in length, except ‹ those ›« when » engaged in diving operations, ‹ shall not be ›« is not » required to exhibit the lights ‹ and ›« or » shapes prescribed in this Rule.

(h) The signals prescribed in this Rule are not signals of vessels in distress and requiring assistance. Such signals are contained in Annex IV to these Rules.

# Rule 28—Vessels Constrained by Their Draft

## International

A vessel constrained by her draft may, in addition to the lights prescribed for power-driven vessels in Rule 23, exhibit where they can best be seen three all-round red lights in a vertical line, or a cylinder.

# Rule 29— Pilot Vessels

(a) A vessel engaged on pilotage duty shall exhibit:
   (i) at or near the masthead, two all-round lights in a vertical line, the upper being white and the lower red;
   (ii) when underway, in addition, sidelights and a sternlight;
   (iii) when at anchor, in addition to the lights prescribed in Rule 29(a)(i), the light, lights, or shape prescribed in Rule 30 for vessels at anchor.

Vessel Engaged on Pilotage Duty
Underway

Vessel Engaged on Pilotage Duty
At anchor; vessel less than 50 meters in length

(b) A pilot vessel when not engaged on pilotage duty shall exhibit the lights or shapes prescribed for a similar vessel of her length.

41

# Rule 30—Anchored Vessels and Vessels Aground

(a) A vessel at anchor shall exhibit where it can best be seen:
(i) in the fore part, an all-round white light or one ball;
(ii) at or near the stern and at a lower level than the light prescribed in Rule 30(a)(i), an all-round white light.

(a) Vessel at anchor with deck illumination

(b) Vessel at anchor -
less than 50 meters in length

## International

**Interpretive Rule—33 CFR 82.5 Lights for moored vessels**

For the purposes of Rule 30 of the 72 COLREGS, a vessel at anchor includes a barge made fast to one or more mooring buoys or other similar device attached to the sea or river floor. Such a barge may be lighted as a vessel at anchor in accordance with Rule 30, or may be lighted on the corners in accordance with 33 CFR 83.30(h) through (l).

## Inland

*Interpretive Rule—33 CFR 90.5 Lights for moored vessels*

*A vessel at anchor includes a vessel made fast to one or more mooring buoys or other similar device attached to the ocean floor. Such vessels may be lighted as a vessel at anchor in accordance with Rule 30, or may be lighted on the corners in accordance with 33 CFR 88.30(h) through (l).*

(b) A vessel of less than 50 meters in length may exhibit an all-round white light where it can best be seen instead of the lights prescribed in Rule 30(a).

(c) A vessel at anchor may, and a vessel of 100 meters and more in length shall, also use the available working or equivalent lights to illuminate her decks.

(d) A vessel aground shall exhibit the lights prescribed in Rule 30(a) or (b) and in addition, if practicable, where they can best be seen: (i) two all-round red lights in a vertical line; (ii) three balls in a vertical line.

Vessel Aground

(e) A vessel of less than 7 meters in length, when at anchor not in or near a narrow channel, fairway or where other vessels normally navigate, shall not be required to exhibit the lights or shape prescribed in Rule 30(a) and (b).

(f) A vessel of less than 12 meters in length, when aground, shall not be required to exhibit the lights or shapes prescribed in Rule 30(d)(i) and (ii).

## Inland

(g) A vessel of less than 20 meters in length, when at anchor in a special anchorage area designated by the Coast Guard, shall not be required to exhibit the anchor lights and shapes required by this Rule.

(h) The following barges shall display at night and if practicable in periods of restricted visibility the lights described in Rule 30(i):
(i) Every barge projecting into a buoyed or restricted channel.
(ii) Every barge so moored that it reduces the available navigable width of any channel to less than 80 meters.
(iii) Barges moored in groups more than two barges wide or to a maximum width of over 25 meters.
(iv) Every barge not moored parallel to the bank or dock.

(i) Barges described in Rule 30(h) shall carry two unobstructed all-round white lights of an intensity to be visible for at least 1 nautical mile and meeting the technical requirements as prescribed in Annex I.

(j) A barge or a group of barges at anchor or made fast to one or more mooring buoys or other similar device, in lieu of the provisions of Rule 30, may carry unobstructed all-round white lights of an intensity to be visible for at least 1 nautical mile that meet the requirements of Annex I and shall be arranged as follows:
(i) Any barge that projects from a group formation, shall be lighted on its outboard corners.
(ii) On a single barge moored in water where other vessels normally navigate on both sides of the barge, lights shall be placed to mark the corner extremities of the barge.
(iii) On barges moored in group formation, moored in water where other vessels normally navigate on both sides of the group, lights shall be placed to mark the corner extremities of the group.

(k) The following are exempt from the requirements of Rule 30: (i) A barge or group of barges moored in a slip or slough used primarily for mooring purposes.
(ii) A barge or group of barges moored behind a pierhead.
(iii) A barge less than 20 meters in length when moored in a special anchorage area designated in accordance with 33 CFR 109.10.

(l) Barges moored in well-illuminated areas are exempt from the lighting requirements of Rule 30. These areas are as follows:

CHICAGO SANITARY SHIP CANAL

| | | |
|---|---|---|
| (1) Mile 293.2 to 293.9 | (10) Mile 305.7 to 305.8 | (19) Mile 316.85 to 317.05 |
| (2) Mile 295.2 to 296.1 | (11) Mile 310.7 to 310.9 | (20) Mile 317.5 |
| (3) Mile 297.5 to 297.8 | (12) Mile 311 to 311.2 | (21) Mile 318.4 to 318.9 |
| (4) Mile 298 to 298.2 | (13) Mile 312.5 to 312.6 | (22) Mile 318.7 to 318.8 |
| (5) Mile 298.6 to 298.8 | (14) Mile 313.8 to 314.2 | (23) Mile 320 to 320.3 |
| (6) Mile 299.3 to 299.4 | (15) Mile 314.6 | (24) Mile 320.6 |
| (7) Mile 299.8 to 300.5 | (16) Mile 314.8 to 315.3 | (25) Mile 322.3 to 322.4 |
| (8) Mile 303 to 303.2 | (17) Mile 315.7 to 316 | (26) Mile 322.8 |
| (9) Mile 303.7 to 303.9 | (18) Mile 316.8 | (27) Mile 322.9 to 327.2 |

CALUMET SAG CHANNEL
(28) Mile 316.5

LITTLE CALUMET RIVER
(29) Mile 321.2

CALUMET RIVER

| | | |
|---|---|---|
| (31) Mile 328.5 to 328.7 | (33) Mile 330 west bank to 330.2 | (35) Mile 332.2 to 332.4 |
| (32) Mile 329.2 to 329.4 | (34) Mile 331.4 to 331.6 | (36) Mile 332.6 to 332.8 |

| CUMBERLAND RIVER | (37) Mile 126.8 | (38) Mile 191 |
|---|---|---|

## Rule 31—Seaplanes

Where it is impracticable for a seaplane or a WIG craft to exhibit lights or shapes of the characteristics or in the positions prescribed in Rules 20 through 31 she shall exhibit lights and shapes as closely similar in characteristics and position as is possible.

# Part D—Sound and Light Signals

## Rule 32—Definitions

(a) The word "whistle" means any sound signaling appliance capable of producing the prescribed blasts and which complies with the specifications in Annex III to these Rules.

(b) The term "short blast" means a blast of about one seconds duration.

(c) The term "prolonged blast" means a blast of from four to six seconds duration.

## Rule 33—Equipment for Sound Signals

(a) A vessel of 12 meters or more in length shall be provided with a whistle, a vessel of 20 meters or more in length shall be provided with a bell in addition to a whistle, and a vessel of 100 meters or more in length shall, in addition be provided with a gong, the tone and sound of which cannot be confused with that of the bell. The whistle, bell and gong shall comply with the specifications in Annex III to these Regulations. The bell or gong or both may be replaced by other equipment having the same respective sound characteristics, provided that manual sounding of the prescribed signals shall always be possible.

(b) A vessel of less than 12 meters in length shall not be obliged to carry the sound signaling appliances prescribed in Rule 33(a) but if she does not, she shall be provided with some other means of making an efficient signal.

# Rule 34—Maneuvering and Warning Signals

| International | Inland |
|---|---|
| (a) When vessels are in sight of one, a power-driven vessel underway, when maneuvering as authorized or required by these Rules, shall indicate that maneuvre by the following signals on her whistle:<br><br>- One short blasts to mean "I am altering my course to starboard"<br>- Two short blasts to mean "I am altering my course to port"<br>- Three short blasts to mean "I am operating astern propulsion" | (a) When power-driven vessels are in sight of one another and meeting or crossing at a distance within half a mile of each other, each vessel underway, when maneuvering as authorized or required by these Rules,<br><br>(i) shall indicate that maneuver by the following signals on her whistle:<br>- One short blasts to mean "I intend to leave you on my port side"<br>- Two short blasts to mean "I intend to leave you on my starboard side"<br>- Three short blasts to mean "I am operating astern propulsion"<br><br>(ii) upon hearing the one or two blast signal of the other shall, if in agreement, sound the same whistle signal and take the steps necessary to effect a safe passing. If, however, from any cause, the vessel doubts the safety of the proposed maneuver, she shall sound the signal specified in Rule 34(d) and each vessel shall take appropriate precautionary action until a safe passing agreement is made. |
| (b) Any vessel may supplement the whistle signals prescribed in Rule 34(a) by light signals, repeated as appropriate, while the maneuver is being carried out:<br><br>(i) these signals shall have the following significance:<br>(ii) the duration of each flash shall be about one second, the interval between flashes shall be about one second, and the interval between successive signals shall not be less than ten seconds.<br>(iii) the light used for this signal shall, if fitted, be an all-round white, visible at a minimum range of 5 miles, and shall comply with the provisions of Annex I to these Regulations.<br><br>- One flash to mean "I am altering my course to starboard"<br>- Two flashes to mean I am altering my course to port"<br>- Three flashes to mean "I am operating astern propulsion" | (b) A vessel may supplement the whistle signals prescribed in Rule 34(a) by light signals:<br><br>(i) these signals shall have the following significance:<br>(ii) the duration of each flash shall be about one second.<br>(iii) the light used for this signal shall, if fitted, be an allround white or yellow, visible at a minimum range of 2 miles, synchronized with the whistle and shall comply with the provisions of Annex I to these Regulations.<br><br>- One flash to mean "I intend to leave you on my port side"<br>- Two flashes to mean "I intend to leave you on my starboard side"<br>- Three flashes to mean "I am operating astern propulsion" |

# Rule 34—Maneuvering and Warning Signals CONTINUED

| International | Inland |
|---|---|
| (c) When in sight of one another in a narrow channel or fairway:<br><br>(i) a vessel intending to overtake another shall in compliance with Rule 9(e)(i) indicate her intention by the following signals on her whistle:<br><br>- Two prolonged blasts followed by one short blast to mean "I intend to overtake you on your starboard side"<br><br>- Two prolonged blasts followed by two short blasts to mean "I intend to overtake you on your port side"<br><br>(ii) the vessel about to be overtaken when acting in accordance with Rule 9(e)(iii) shall indicate her agreement by the following signal on her whistle: one prolonged, one short, one prolonged and one short blast, in that order. | (c) When in sight of one another:<br><br>(i) a power-driven vessel intending to overtake another power-driven vessel shall indicate her intention by the following signals on her whistle:<br><br>- One short blast to mean "I intend to overtake you on your starboard side"<br><br>- Two short blasts to mean "I intend to overtake you on your port side"<br><br>(ii) the power-driven vessel about to be overtaken shall, if in agreement, sound a similar sound signal. If in doubt she shall sound the signal prescribed in Rule 34(d). |
| (d) When vessels in sight of one another are approaching each other and from any cause either vessel fails to understand the intentions or actions of the other, or is in doubt whether sufficient action is being taken by the other to avoid collision, the vessel in doubt shall immediately indicate such doubt by giving at least five short and rapid blasts on the whistle. Such signal may be supplemented by at least five short and rapid flashes. | (d) When vessels in sight of one another are approaching each other and from any cause either vessel fails to understand the intentions or actions of the other, or is in doubt whether sufficient action is being taken by the other to avoid collision, the vessel in doubt shall immediately indicate such doubt by giving at least five short and rapid blasts on the whistle. Such signal may be supplemented by at least five short and rapid flashes. |
| (e) A vessel nearing a bend or an area of a channel or fairway where other vessels may be obscured by an intervening obstruction shall sound one prolonged blast. This signal shall be answered with a prolonged blast by any approaching vessel that may be within hearing around the bend or behind the intervening obstruction. | (e) A vessel nearing a bend or an area of a channel or fairway where other vessels may be obscured by an intervening obstruction shall sound one prolonged blast. This signal shall be answered with a prolonged blast by any approaching vessel that may be within hearing around the bend or behind the intervening obstruction. |
| (f) If whistles are fitted on a vessel at a distance apart of more than 100 meters, one whistle only shall be used for giving maneuvering and warning signals. | (f) If whistles are fitted on a vessel at a distance apart of more than 100 meters, one whistle only shall be used for giving maneuvering and warning signals. |
| | (g) When a power-driven vessel is leaving a dock or berth, she shall sound one prolonged blast. |
| | (h) A vessel that reaches agreement with another vessel in a head-on, crossing, or overtaking situation, as for example, by using the radiotelephone as prescribed by the Vessel Bridge-to-Bridge Radiotelephone Act (85 Stat. 164; 33 U.S.C. 1201 et seq.), is not obliged to sound the whistle signals prescribed by this Rule, but may do so. If agreement is not reached, then whistle signals shall be exchanged in a timely manner and shall prevail. |

# Rule 35—Sound Signals in Restricted Visibility

In or near an area of restricted visibility, whether by day or night the signals prescribed in this Rule shall be used as follows: (a) A power-driven vessel making way through the water shall sound at intervals of not more than 2 minutes one prolonged blast.

(b) A power-driven vessel underway but stopped and making no way through the water shall sound at intervals of no more than 2 minutes two prolonged blasts in succession with an interval of about 2 seconds between them.

(c) A vessel not under command, a vessel restricted in her ability to maneuver « whether underway or at anchor », ‹ a vessel constrained by her draft › , a sailing vessel, a vessel engaged in fishing whether underway or at anchor and a vessel engaged in towing or pushing another vessel shall, instead of the signals prescribed in Rule 35(a) or (b), sound at intervals of not more than 2 minutes three blasts in succession, namely one prolonged followed by two short blasts.

## International

(d) A vessel engaged in fishing, when at anchor, and a vessel restricted in her ability to maneuver when carrying out her work at anchor, shall instead of the signals prescribed in Rule 35(g) sound the signal prescribed in Rule 35(c).

(e) A vessel towed or if more than one vessel is towed the last vessel of the tow, if manned, shall at intervals of not more than 2 minutes sound four blasts in succession, namely one prolonged followed by three short blasts. When practicable, this signal shall be made immediately after the signal made by the towing vessel.

(f) When a pushing vessel and a vessel being pushed ahead are rigidly connected in a composite unit they shall be regarded as a power-driven vessel and shall give the signals prescribed in Rule 35(a) or (b).

(g) A vessel at anchor shall at intervals of not more than 1 minute ring the bell rapidly for about 5 sec-onds. In a vessel 100 meters or more in length the bell shall be sounded in the forepart of the vessel and immediately after the ringing of the bell the gong shall be sounded rapidly for about 5 seconds in the after part of the vessel. A vessel at anchor may in addition sound three blasts in succession, namely one short, one prolonged and one short blast, to give warning of her position and of the possibility of collision to an approaching vessel.

(h) A vessel aground shall give the bell signal and if required the gong signal prescribed in Rule 35(g) and shall, in addition, give three separate and distinct strokes on the bell immediately before and af-ter the rapid ringing of the bell. A vessel aground may in addition sound an appropriate whistle signal.

(i) A vessel of 12 meters or more but less than 20 meters in length shall not be obliged to give the bell signals prescribed in Rule 35(g) and (h). However, if she does not, she shall make some other efficient sound signal at intervals of not more than 2 minutes.

(j) A vessel of less than 12 meters in length shall not be obliged to give the above mentioned signals but, if she does not, shall make some other efficient sound signal at intervals of not more than 2 minutes.

(k) A pilot vessel when engaged on pilotage duty may, in addition to the signals prescribed in Rule 35(a), (b) or (g), sound an identity signal consisting of four short blasts.

## Inland

(l) The following vessels shall not be required to sound signals as prescribed in Rule 35(g) when anchored in a special anchorage area designated by the Coast Guard:
　　(i) a vessel of less than 20 meters in length; and
　　(ii) a barge, canal boat, scow, or other nondescript craft.

## Rule 36—Signals to Attract Attention

If necessary to attract the attention of another vessel, any vessel may make light or sound signals that cannot be mistaken for any signal authorized elsewhere in these Rules, or may direct the beam of her searchlight in the direction of the danger, in such a way as not to embarrass any vessel.

### International

Any light to attract the attention of another vessel shall be such that it cannot be mistaken for any aid to navigation. For the purpose of this Rule the use of high intensity intermittent or revolving lights, such as strobe lights, shall be avoided.

## Rule 37—Distress Signals

When a vessel is in distress and requires assistance she shall use or exhibit the signals described in Annex IV to these Rules.

## Annex IV—Distress Signals

### 1. « *Need of assistance* »

The following signals, used or exhibited either together or separately, indicate distress and need of assistance:

(a) a gun or other explosive signal fired at intervals of about a minute;

(b) a continuous sounding with any fog-signaling apparatus;

(c) rockets or shells, throwing red stars fired one at a time at short intervals;

(d) a signal made by any signaling method consisting of the group . . . – – – . . . (SOS) in the Morse Code;

(e) a signal sent by radiotelephony consisting of the spoken word "Mayday";

(f) the International Code Signal of distress indicated by N.C.;

(g) a signal consisting of a square flag having above or below it a ball or anything resembling a ball;

(h) flames on the vessel (as from a burning tar barrel, oil barrel, etc.);

(i) a rocket parachute flare or a hand flare showing a red light;

(j) a smoke signal giving off orange-colored smoke;

(k) slowly and repeatedly raising and lowering arms outstretched to each side;

(l) a distress alert by means of digital selective calling (DSC) transmitted on:

(i) VHF channel 70, or

(ii) MF/HF on the frequencies 2187.5 kHz, 8414.5 kHz, 4207.5 kHz, 6312 kHz, 12577 kHz or 16804.5 kHz;

(m) a ship-to-shore distress alert transmitted by the ship's Inmarsat or other mobile satellite service provider ship earth station;

(n) signals transmitted by emergency position-indicating radio beacons;

(o) approved signals transmitted by radiocommunication systems, including survival craft radar transponders « *'meeting the requirements of 47 CFR 80.1095 {search and rescue locating devices}* ».

« *(p) A high intensity white light flashing at regular intervals from 50 to 70 times per minute.* »

## 2. ‹‹ *Exclusive use* ››

The use or exhibition of any of the foregoing signals except for the purpose of indicating distress and need of assistance and the use of other signals which may be confused with any of the above signals is prohibited.

## 3. ‹‹ *Supplemental signals* ››

Attention is drawn to the relevant sections of the International Code of Signals, the International Aeronautical and Maritime Search and Rescue Manual, Volume III, ‹ the International Telecommunication Union Radio Regulations, › and the following signals:

(a) A piece of orange-colored canvas with either a black square and circle or other appropriate symbol (for identification from the air);

(b) A dye marker.

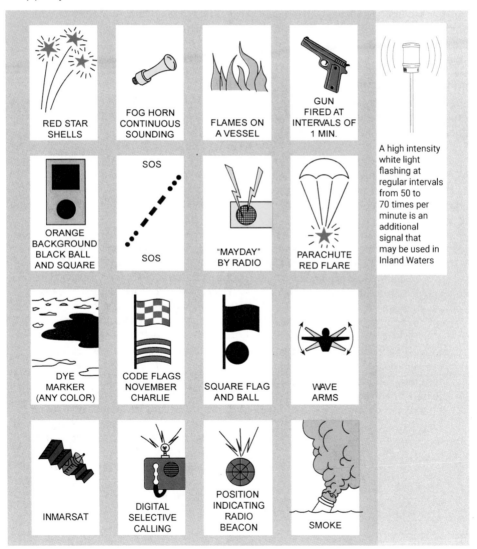

# Part E—Exemptions

## Rule 38—Exemptions

| International | Inland |
|---|---|
| Any vessel (or class of vessel) provided that she complies with the requirements of — the International Regulations for the Preventing of Collisions at Sea, 1960, the keel of which is laid or is at a corresponding stage of construction before the entry into force of these Regulations may be exempted from compliance therewith as follows: | *Any vessel or class of vessels, the keel of which was laid or which is at a corresponding stage of construction before December 24, 1980, provided that she complies with the requirements of—* |
| (a) The installation of lights with ranges prescribed in Rule 22, until 4 years after the date of entry into force of these Regulations. | *(a) The Act of June 7, 1897 (30 Stat. 96), as amended (33 U.S.C. 154-232) for vessels navigating the waters subject to that statute;* |
| (b) The installation of lights with color specifications as prescribed in §7 of Annex I to these Regulations, until 4 years after the entry into force of these Regulations. | *(b) §4233 of the Revised Statutes (33 U.S.C. 301-356) for vessels navigating the waters subject to that statute;* |
| (c) The repositioning of lights as a result of conversion from Imperial to metric units and rounding off measurement figures, permanent exemption. | *(c) The Act of February 8, 1895 (28 Stat. 645), as amended (33 U.S.C. 241-295) for vessels navigating the waters subject to that statute; or* |
| (d) (i) The repositioning of masthead lights on vessels of less than 150 meters in length, resulting from the prescriptions of §3 (a) of Annex I to these Regulations, permanent exemption.<br><br>(ii) The repositioning of masthead lights on vessels of 150 meters or more in length, resulting from the prescriptions of §3 (a) of Annex I to these Regulations, until 9 years after the date of entry into force of these Regulations. | *(d) §§3, 4, and 5 of the Act of April 25, 1940 (54 Stat. 163), as amended (46 U.S.C. 526 b, c, and d) for motorboats navigating the waters subject to that statute; shall be exempted from compliance with the technical Annexes to these Rules as follows:*<br><br>*(i) The installation of lights with ranges prescribed in Rule 22, vessels of less than 20 meters in length are permanently exempt;*<br><br>*(ii) The installation of lights with color specifications as prescribed in §7 of Annex I to these Rules, until 4 years after the effective date of the Inland Navigational Rules Act of 1980 (Pub. L. 96-591), except that vessels of less than 20 meters in length are permanently exempt;* |

| International | Inland |
|---|---|
| | (d) (iii) The repositioning of lights as a result of a conversion to metric units and rounding off of measurement figures, are permanently exempt. |
| | (iv) The horizontal repositioning of masthead lights prescribed by Annex I to these Rules, vessels of less than 150 meters in length are permanently exempted. |
| | (v) Power-driven vessels of 12 meters or more but less than 20 meters in length are permanently exempt from the provisions of Rule 23(a)(i) and 23(a)(iv) provided that, in place of these lights, the vessel exhibits a white light aft visible all-around the horizon. |
| (e) The repositioning of masthead lights resulting from the prescriptions of §2(b) of Annex I to these Regulations, until 9 years after the date of entry into force of these Regulations. | |
| (f) The repositioning of sidelights resulting from the prescriptions of §2(g) and 3(b) of Annex I to these Regulations, until 9 years after the date of entry into force of these Regulations. | |
| (g) The requirements for sound signal appliances prescribed in Annex II to these Regulations, until 9 years after the date of entry into force of these Regulations. | |
| (h) The repositioning of all-round lights resulting from the prescription of §9(b) of Annex I to these Regulations, permanent exemption. | |

## International

**Implementing Rule—33 CFR 81.20 Lights and sound signal appliances.**

Each vessel under the 72 COLREGS, except the vessels of the Navy, is exempt from the requirements of the 72 COLREGS to the limitation for the period of time stated in Rule 38 (a), (b), (c), (d), (e), (f), and (g) if:

(a) Her keel is laid or is at a corresponding stage of construction before July 15, 1977; and

(b) She meets the International Regulations for Preventing Collisions at Sea, 1960 (77 Stat. 194, 33 U.S.C. 1051-1094).

# Part F—Verification of Compliance with the Provisions of the Convention

## Rule 39—Definitions

### International

(a) "Audit" means a systematic, independent and documented process for obtaining audit evidence and evaluating it objectively to determine the extent to which audit criteria are fulfilled.

(b) "Audit Scheme" means the IMO Member State Audit Scheme established by the Organization and taking into account the guidelines developed by the Organization*.

(c) "Code for Implementation" means the IMO Instruments Implementation Code (III Code) adopted by the Organization by resolution A.1070(28).

(d) "Audit Standard" means the Code for Implementation.

## Rule 40—Application

### International

Contracting Parties shall use the provisions of the Code for Implementation in the execution of their obligations and responsibilities contained in the present Convention.

## Rule 41—Verification of Compliance

### International

(a) Every Contracting Party shall be subject to periodic audits by the Organization in accordance with the audit standard to verify compliance with and implementation of the present Convention.

(b) The Secretary-General of the Organization shall have responsibility for administering the Audit Scheme, based on the guidelines developed by the Organization*.

(c) Every Contracting Party shall have responsibility for facilitating the conduct of the audit and implementation of a programme of actions to address the findings, based on the guidelines developed by the Organization*.

(d) Audit of all Contracting Parties shall be:
(i) based on an overall schedule developed by the Secretary-General of the Organization, taking into account the guidelines developed by the Organization*; and
(ii) conducted at periodic intervals, taking into account the guidelines developed by the Organization*.

* Refer to the Framework and Procedures for the IMO Member State Audit Scheme, adopted by the Organization by resolution A.1067(28).

# Annex I—Positioning and Technical Details of Lights and Shapes

## Definitions

(a) The term "height above the hull" means height above the uppermost continuous deck. This height shall be measured from the position vertically beneath the location of the light.

### Inland

(b) High-speed craft means a craft capable of maximum speed in meters per second (m/s) equal to or exceeding:

$3.7\nabla^{0.1667}$; where $\nabla$ =displacement corresponding to the design waterline (cubic meters).

Note: The same formula expressed in pounds and knots is maximum speed in knots (kts) equal to exceeding $1.98(lbs)\ 3.7\nabla^{0.1667}$; where $\nabla$ =displacement corresponding to design waterline in pounds.

(c) The term "practical cut-off" means, for vessels 20 meters or more in length, 12.5 percent of the minimum luminous intensity (Table 14(b)) corresponding to the greatest range of visibility for which the requirements of Annex I are met.

(d) The term "Rule" or "Rules" has the same meaning as in Rule 3(r).

## Vertical Positioning and Spacing of Lights

(a) On a power-driven vessel of 20 meters or more in length the masthead light shall be placed as follows:

(i) The forward masthead light, or if only one masthead light is carried, then that light, at a height above the hull of not less than ‹ 6 ›« 5 » meters, and, if the breadth of the vessel exceeds ‹ 6 ›« 5 » meters, then at a height above the hull not less than such breadth, so however that the light need not be placed at a greater height above the hull than ‹ 12 ›« 8 » meters;

(ii) when two masthead lights are carried the after one shall be at least ‹ 4.5 ›« 2 » meters vertically higher than the forward one.

(b) The vertical separation of the masthead lights of power-driven vessels shall be such that in all normal conditions of trim the after light will be seen over and separate from the forward light at a distance of 1000 meters from the stem when viewed from ‹ sea › « water » level.

(c) The masthead light of a power-driven vessel of 12 meters but less than 20 meters in length shall be placed at a height above the gunwale of not less than 2.5 meters.

# Vertical Positioning and Spacing of Lights CONTINUED

| International | Inland |
|---|---|
| (d) A power-driven vessel of less than 12 meters in length may carry the uppermost light at a height of less than 2.5 meters above the gunwale. When, however, a masthead light is carried in addition to sidelights and a sternlight or the all-round light prescribed in Rule 23(d)(i) is carried in addition to sidelights, then such masthead light or all-round light shall be carried at least 1 meter higher than the sidelights. | *(d) The masthead light, or the all-round light described in Rule 23(d), of a power-driven vessel of less than 12 meters in length shall be carried at least 1 meter higher than the sidelights.* |

(e) One of the two or three masthead lights prescribed for a power-driven vessel when engaged in towing or pushing another vessel shall be placed in the same position as either the forward masthead light or the after masthead light, provided that ‹ , if carried on the after mast, › the lowest after masthead light shall be at least ‹ 4.5 › « 2 » meters vertically higher than the « *highest* » forward masthead light.

(f) (i) The masthead lights or lights prescribed in Rule 23(a) shall be so placed as to be above and clear of all other lights and obstructions except as described in §(f)(ii).
(ii) When it is impracticable to carry the all-round lights prescribed by Rule 27(b)(i) ‹ or Rule 28 › below the masthead lights, they may be carried above the after masthead light(s) or vertically in between the forward masthead light(s) and after masthead light(s), provided that in the latter case the requirement of §3(c) shall be complied with.

(g) The sidelights of a power-driven vessel shall be placed at ‹ a height above the hull not greater than three quarters of that › « *least 1 meter lower* » of ‹ the › « *than* » forward masthead light. They shall not be so low as to be interfered with by deck lights.

## International

(h) The sidelights, if in a combined lantern and carried on a power-driven vessel of less than 20 meters in length, shall be placed not less than 1 meter below the masthead light.

(i) When the Rules prescribe two or three lights to be carried in a vertical line, they shall be spaced as follows:
(i) On a vessel of 20 meters in length or more such lights shall be spaced not less than ‹ 2 ›« 1 » meter apart, and the lowest of these lights shall, except where a towing light is required, be placed at a height of not less than 4 meters above the hull.
(ii) On a vessel of less than 20 meters in length such lights shall be spaced not less than 1 meter apart and the lowest of these lights shall, except where a towing light is required, be placed at a height of not less than 2 meters above the gunwale.
(iii) When three lights are carried they shall be equally spaced.

(j) The lower of the two all-round lights prescribed for a vessel when engaged in fishing shall be at a height above the sidelights not less than twice the distance between the two vertical lights.

(k) The forward anchor light prescribed in Rule 30(a)(i), when two are carried, shall not be less than 4.5 meters above the after one. On a vessel of 50 meters or more in length this forward anchor light shall be placed at a height or not less than 6 meters above the hull.

## Horizontal Positioning and Spacing of Lights

(a) Except as specified in paragraph (e) of this section, when two masthead lights are prescribed for a power-driven vessel, the horizontal distance between them ‹ shall › « *must* » not be less than one quarter of the length of the vessel but need not be more than 50 meters. The forward light ‹ shall › « *must* » be placed not more than one half of the length of the vessel from the stem.

(b) On a power-driven vessel of 20 meters or more in length the sidelights shall not be placed in front of the forward masthead lights. They shall be placed at or near the side of the vessel.

(c) When the lights prescribed in Rule 27(b)(i) ‹ or Rule 28 › are placed vertically between the forward masthead light(s) and the after masthead light(s), these allround lights shall be placed at a horizontal distance of not less than 2 meters from the fore and aft center-line of the vessel in the athwartship direction.

(d) When only one masthead light is prescribed for a power-driven vessel, this light must be exhibited forward of amidships. For a vessel of less than 20 meters in length, the vessel shall exhibit one masthead light as far forward as is practicable.

### Inland

*(e) On power-driven vessels 50 meters but less than 60 meters in length operated on the Western Rivers, and those { waters specified by the Secretary }, the horizontal distance between masthead lights shall not be less than 10 meters.*

## Details of Location of Direction-Indicating Lights for Fishing Vessels, Dredgers and Vessels Engaged in Underwater Operations

(a) The light indicating the direction of the outlying gear from a vessel engaged in fishing as prescribed in Rule 26(c)(ii) shall be placed at a horizontal distance of not less than 2 meters and not more than 6 meters away from the two all-round red and white lights. This light shall be placed not higher than the all-round white light prescribed in Rule 26(c)(i) and not lower than the sidelights.

(b) The lights and shapes on a vessel engaged in dredging or underwater operations to indicate the obstructed side and/or the side on which it is safe to pass, as prescribed in Rule 27(d)(i) and (ii), shall be placed at the maximum practical horizontal distance, but in no case less than 2 meters, from the lights or shapes prescribed in Rule 27(b)(i) and (ii). In no case shall the upper of these lights or shapes be at a greater height than the lower of the three lights or shapes prescribed in Rule 27(b)(i) and (ii).

## Screens ‹ for sidelights ›

‡ (a) The sidelights of vessels of 20 meters or more in length shall be fitted with ‹ inboard screens painted › matt black, « *inboard screens* » and meet ‹ ing › the requirements of §9‡15. On vessels of less than 20 meters in length, the sidelights, if necessary to meet the requirements of §9‡15, shall be fitted with ‹ inboard › matt black « *inboard* » screens. With a combined lantern, using a single vertical filament and a very narrow division between the green and red sections, external screens need not be fitted.

### Inland

*(b) On power-driven vessels less than 12 meters in length constructed after July 31, 1983, the masthead light, or the all-round light described in Rule 23(d) shall be screened to prevent direct illumination of the vessel forward of the operator's position.*

## Shapes

(a) Shapes shall be black and of the following sizes:
    (i) A ball shall have a diameter of not less than 0.6 meter;
    (ii) a cone shall have a base diameter of not less than 0.6 meter‹s› and a height equal to its diameter;
    ‹ (iii) a cylinder shall have a diameter of at least 0.6 meter and a height of twice its diameter; ›
    (iv)‡(iii) a diamond shape shall consist of two cones as defined in §(a)(ii) having a common base.

(b) The vertical distance between shapes shall be at least 1.5 meter ‹ s ›.

(c) In a vessel of less than 20 meters in length shapes of lesser dimensions but commensurate with the size of the vessel may be used and the distance apart may be correspondingly reduced.

## [7‡13]. Color specification of lights

(a) The chromaticity of all navigation lights shall conform to the following standards, which lie within the boundaries of the area of the diagram specified for each color by the International Commission on Illumination (CIE). ‹ , in the "Colors of Light Signals", which is incorporated by reference. It is Publication CIE No. 2.2. (TC-1.6), 1975, and is available from the Illumination Engineering Society, 345 East 47th Street, New York, NY 10017 and is available for inspection at the Coast Guard, Shore Infrastructure Logistics Center, Aids to Navigation and Marine Environmental Response Product Line (CG-SILC-ATON/MER), 2703 Martin Luther King, Jr. Ave SE, Mailstop 7714, Washington, DC 20593-7714. It is also available for inspection at the National Archives and Records Administration (NARA). For information on the availability of this material at NARA, call 202−741−6030, or go to: http://www.archives.gov/federal_register/code_of_federal_ regulations/ibr_locations.html. This incorporation by reference was approved by the Director of the Federal Register. ›

(b) The boundaries of the area for each color are given by indicating the corner coordinates, which are as follows:

(i) White:

| x | 0.525 | 0.525 | 0.452 | 0.310 | 0.310 | 0.443 |
|---|-------|-------|-------|-------|-------|-------|
| y | 0.382 | 0.440 | 0.440 | 0.348 | 0.283 | 0.382 |

(ii) Green:

| x | 0.028 | 0.009 | 0.300 | 0.203 |
|---|-------|-------|-------|-------|
| y | 0.385 | 0.723 | 0.511 | 0.356 |

(iii) Red:

| x | 0.680 | 0.660 | 0.735 | 0.721 |
|---|-------|-------|-------|-------|
| y | 0.320 | 0.320 | 0.265 | 0.259 |

(iv) Yellow:

| x | 0.612 | 0.618 | 0.575 | 0.575 |
|---|-------|-------|-------|-------|
| y | 0.382 | 0.382 | 0.425 | 0.406 |

## [8‡14]. Intensity of Lights

(a) The minimum luminous intensity of lights shall be calculated by using the formula:
$I = 3.43 \times 106 \times T \times D2 \times K\text{-}D$ where:

I is luminous intensity in candelas under service conditions,

T is threshold factor $2 \times 10\text{-}7$ lux,

D is range of visibility (luminous range) of the light in nautical miles,

K is atmospheric transmissivity. For prescribed lights the value of K shall be 0.8, corresponding to a meteorological visibility of approximately 13 nautical miles.

(b) A selection of figures derived from the formula is given in the following table:

| Range of visibility (luminous range) of light in nautical miles D | Minimum luminous intensity of light in candelas for K=0.8 I |
|---|---|
| 1 | .09 |
| 2 | 4.3 |
| 3 | 1.2 |
| 4 | 27 |
| 5 | 52 |
| 6 | 94 |

‹ Note: The maximum luminous intensity of navigation lights should be limited to avoid undue glare. This shall not be achieved by a variable control of the luminous intensity. ›

## [9‡15]. Horizontal Sectors

(a) (i) In the forward direction, sidelights as fitted on the vessel shall show the minimum required intensities. The intensities shall decrease to reach practical cutoff between 1 and one degrees outside the prescribed sectors.

(ii) For sternlights and masthead lights and at 22.5 degrees abaft the beam for side lights, the minimum required intensities shall be maintained over the arc of the horizon up to 5 degrees within the limits of the sectors prescribed in Rule 21. From 5 degrees within the prescribed sectors the intensity may decrease by 50 percent up to the prescribed limits; it shall decrease steadily to reach practical cut-off at not more than 5 degrees outside the prescribed sectors.

(b) (i) All-round lights shall be so located as not to be obscured by masts, topmasts or structures within angular sectors of more than 6 degrees, except anchor lights prescribed in Rule 30, which need not be placed at an impracticable height above the hull « , *and the allround white light described in Rule 23(e), which maynot be obscured at all* ».

(ii) If it is impracticable to comply with §(b)(i) by exhibiting only one all-round light, two all-round lights shall be used suitably positioned or screened so that they « *to* » appear, as far as practicable, as one light at a « *minimum* » distance of 1 « *nautical* » mile.

« *Note: Two unscreened all-round lights that are 1.28 meters apart or less will appear as one light to the naked eye at a distance of 1 nautical mile.* »

## [10‡16]. Vertical Sectors

(a) The vertical sectors of electric lights as fitted, with the exception of lights on sailing vessels underway «*and on unmanned barges*», shall ensure that:

(i) At least the required minimum intensity is maintained at all angles from 5 degrees above to 5 degrees below the horizontal;

(ii) at least 60 percent of the required minimum intensity is maintained from 7.5 degrees above to 7.5 degrees below the horizontal

(b) In the case of sailing vessels underway the vertical sectors of electric lights as fitted shall ensure that:

(i) At least the required minimum intensity is maintained at all angles from 5 degrees above to 5 degrees below the horizontal;

(ii) at least 50 percent of the required minimum intensity is maintained from 25 degrees above to 25 degrees below the horizontal

### Inland

*(c) In the case of unmanned barges the minimum required intensity of electric lights as fitted shall be maintained on the horizontal.*

(c)‡(d) In the case of lights other than electric lights these specifications shall be met as closely as possible.

## [11‡17]. Intensity of Non-electric Lights

Non-electric lights shall so far as practicable comply with the minimum intensities, as specified in the « *Intensity of Lights* » Table.

## [12‡18]. Maneuvering Light

<< *Notwithstanding the provisions of §2(f)* >>, the maneuvering light described in Rule 34(b) shall be placed << *approximately* >> in the same fore and aft vertical plane as the masthead light or lights and, where practicable, at a minimum height of [2‡1.5] meter vertically above the forward masthead light, provided that it shall be carried not less than [2‡1.5] meter vertically above or below the after masthead light. On a vessel where only one masthead light is carried, the maneuvering light, if fitted, shall be carried where it can best be seen, not less than [2‡1.5] meters vertically apart from the masthead light.

## [13‡19]. High Speed Craft

(a) The masthead light of high-speed craft may be placed at a height related to the breadth « *of the craft* » lower than that prescribed in §2(a)(i), provided that the base angle of the isosceles triangle formed by the sidelights and masthead light when seen in end elevation is not less than 27 degrees.

(b) On high-speed craft of 50 meters or more in length, the vertical separation between foremast and mainmast light of 4.5 meters required by §‹ 2(a)(ii) › « *2(k)* » may be modified provided that such distance shall not be less than the value determined by the following formula:

$$y = \frac{(a+17\Psi)C}{1000} + 2$$

where:

y the height of the mainmast light above the foremast light in meters;

a is the height of the foremast light above the water surface in service condition in meters;

Ψ is the trim in service condition in degrees;

C is the horizontal separation of masthead lights in meters.

Note: Refer to the International Code of Safety for High-Speed Craft, 1994 and the International Code of Safety for High-Speed Craft, 2000.

## [14‡20]. Approval

The construction of lights and shapes and the installation of lights on board the vessel ‹ shall be to the satisfaction of the appropriate authority of the State whose flag the vessel is entitled to fly › « *must satisfy the Commandant, U. S. Coast Guard* ».

## Annex II—Additional Signals for Fishing Vessels Fishing in Close Proximity

## See Rule 26(f).

# Annex III—Technical Details of Sound Signal Appliances

## 1. Whistles

(a) Frequencies and range of audibility. The fundamental frequency of the signal shall lie within the range 70-700 Hz. The range of audibility of the signal from a whistle shall be determined by those frequencies, which may include the fundamental and/or one or more higher frequencies, which lie within the range 180-700 Hz (+/- 1 percent) for a vessel of 20 meters or more in length, or 180-2100 Hz (+/- 1 percent) for a vessel of less than 20 meters in length and which provide the sound pressure levels specified in §1(c).

(b) Limits of fundamental frequencies. To ensure a wide variety of whistle characteristics, the fundamental frequency of a whistle shall be between the following limits:
(i) 70-200 Hz, for a vessel 200 meters or more in length;
(ii) 130-350 Hz, for a vessel 75 meters but less than 200 meters in length;
(iii) 250-700 Hz, for a vessel less than 75 meters in length.

(c) Sound signal intensity and range of audibility. A whistle fitted in a vessel shall provide, in the direction of maximum intensity of the whistle and at a distance of 1 meter from it, a sound pressure level in at least one onethird octave band within the range of frequencies 180-700 Hz (+/- 1 percent) for a vessel of 20 meters ‹ or more in length, or 180-2100 Hz (+/- 1 percent) for a vessel of less than 20 meters in length ›, of not less than the appropriate figure given in the table below.

| Length of vessel in meters | One-third octave band level at 1 meter in dB referred to $2 \times 10^{-5}N/m^2$ | Audibility range in nautical miles |
|---|---|---|
| 200 or more | 143 | 2 |
| 75 but less than 200 | 138 | 1.5 |
| 20 but less than 75 | 130 | 1 |
| Less than 20 | 120* | 0.5 |
| | 115** | |
| | 111*** | |

\* When the measured frequencies lie within the range 180-450 Hz
** When the measured frequencies lie within the range 450-800 Hz
*** When the measured frequencies lie within the range 800-2100 Hz

The range of audibility in the table is for information and is approximately the range at which a whistle may be heard on its forward axis with 90 percent probability in conditions of still air on board a vessel having average background noise level at the listening posts (taken to be 68 dB in the octave band centered on 250 Hz and 63 dB in the octave band centered on 500 Hz). « It is shown for informational purposes only. » In practice, the range at which a whistle may be heard is extremely variable and depends critically on weather conditions; the values given can be regarded as typical but under conditions of strong wind or high ambient noise level at the listening post the range may be reduced.

(d) Directional properties. The sound pressure level of a directional whistle shall be not more than 4 dB below the ‹ prescribed › sound pressure level ‹ on the axis at ›, « specified in §(c) » any direction in the horizontal plane within +/- 45 degrees of the axis. The sound pressure level ‹ at › « of the whistle in » any other direction in the horizontal plane shall be not more than 10 dB ‹ below the prescribed sound pressure level on › « less than the sound pressure level specified for » the forward axis, so that the range « audibility » in any direction will be at least half the range « *required* » on the forward axis. The sound pressure level shall be measured in that one-third octave band which determines the audibility range.

(e) Positioning of whistles.
(i) When a directional whistle is to be used as the only whistle on ‹ a vessel, it shall be installed with its maximum intensity directed straight ahead › « *the vessel and is permanently installed, it shall be installed with its forward axis directed forward* ».
(ii) A whistle shall be placed as high as practicable on a vessel, in order to reduce interception of the emitted sound by obstructions and also to minimize hearing damage risk to personnel. The sound pressure level of the vessel's own signal at listening posts shall not exceed 110 dB(A) and so far as practicable should not exceed 100 dB(A).

(f) Fitting of more than one whistle. If whistles are fitted at a distance apart of more than 100 meters, ‹ it shall be so arranged that they are › « *they shall* » not « *be* » sounded simultaneously.

| International | Inland |
| --- | --- |
| (g) Combined whistle systems.<br><br>If due to the presence of obstructions the sound field of a single whistle or of one of the whistles referred to in §(f) is likely to have a zone of greatly reduced signal level, it is recommended that a combined whistle system be fitted so as to overcome this reduction. The whistles of a combined system shall be located at a distance apart of not more than 100 meters and arranged to be sounded simultaneously. The frequency of any one whistle shall differ from those of the others by at least 10 Hz. | *(g) Combined whistle systems.*<br><br>*(i) A combined whistle system is a number of whistles (sound emitting sources) operated together. For the purposes of the Rules of Sub-chapter E a combined whistle system is to be regarded as a single whistle.*<br><br>*(ii) The whistles of a combined system shall:*<br>*(1) Be located at a distance apart of not more than 100 meters;*<br>*(2) Be sounded simultaneously;*<br>*(3) Each have a fundamental frequency different from those of the others by at least 10 Hz; and*<br>*(4) Have a tonal characteristic appropriate for the length of vessel which shall be evidenced by at least two-thirds of the whistles in the combined system having fundamental frequencies falling within the limits prescribed in paragraph (b) of this section, or if there are only two whistles in the combined system, by the higher fundamental frequency falling within the limits prescribed in paragraph (b) of this section.*<br><br>*Note to paragraph (g): If, due to the presence of obstructions, the sound field of a single whistle or of one of the whistles referred to in paragraph*<br><br>*(f) of this section is likely to have a zone of greatly reduced signal level, a combined whistle system should be fitted so as to overcome this reduction.*<br><br>*(h) Towing vessel whistles.*<br>*A power-driven vessel normally engaged in pushing ahead or towing alongside may, at all times, use a whistle whose characteristic falls within the limits prescribed by §1(b) for the longest customary composite length of the vessel and its tow.* |

## 2. Bell or gong

(a) Intensity of signal. A bell or gong, or other device having similar sound characteristics shall produce a sound pressure level of not less than 110 dB at ‹ a distance of › 1 meter ‹ from it ›.

(b) Construction. Bells and gongs shall be made of corrosion-resistant material and designed to give clear tone. The diameter of the mouth of the bell shall be not less than 300 mm for vessels of 20 meters or more in length. Where practicable, a power-driven bell striker is recommended to ensure constant force but manual operation shall be possible. The mass of the striker shall be not less than 3 percent of the mass of the bell.

### International

### 3. Approval

The construction of sound signal appliances, their performance and their installation on board the vessel shall be to the satisfaction of the appropriate authority of the State whose flag the vessel is entitled to fly.

## Annex IV—Distress Signals

### {At Rule 37}

## Annex V—Pilot Rules

### §88.01 Purpose and applicability.

This part applies to all vessels operating on United States inland waters and to United States vessels operating on the Canadian waters of the Great Lakes to the extent there is no conflict with Canadian law.

### §88.03 Definitions.

The terms used in this part have the same meaning as the terms defined in part 83 of this subchapter.

### §88.05 Law enforcement vessels.

(a) Law enforcement vessels may display a flashing blue light when engaged in direct law enforcement or public safety activities. This light must be located so that it does not interfere with the visibility of the vessel's navigation lights.

(b) The blue light described in this section may be displayed by law enforcement vessels of the United States and the States and their political subdivisions.

### §88.07 Public safety activities.

(a) Vessels engaged in government sanctioned public safety activities, and commercial vessels performing similar functions, may display an alternately flashing red and yellow light signal. This identification light signal must be located so that it does not interfere with the visibility of the vessel's navigation lights. The identification light signal may be used only as an identification signal and conveys no special privilege. Vessels using the identification light signal during public safety activities must abide by the Inland Navigation Rules, and must not presume that the light or the exigency gives them precedence or right of way.

(b) Public safety activities include but are not limited to patrolling marine parades, regattas, or special water celebrations; traffic control; salvage; firefighting; medical assistance; assisting disabled vessels; and search and rescue.

# Part 81—72 COLREGS: IMPLEMENTING RULES

## §81.1 Definitions.

As used in this part:

72 COLREGS refers to the International Regulations for Preventing Collisions at Sea, 1972, done at London, October 20, 1972, as rectified by the Proces-Verbal of December 1, 1973, as amended.

*A vessel of special construction or purpose* means a vessel designed or modified to perform a special function and whose arrangement is thereby made relatively inflexible.

*Interference with the special function of the vessel* occurs when installation or use of lights, shapes, or sound-signaling appliances under 72 COLREGS prevents or significantly hinders the operation in which the vessel is usually engaged.

## §81.3 General.

Vessels of special construction or purpose which cannot fully comply with the light, shape, and sound signal provisions of 72 COLREGS without interfering with their special function may instead meet alternative requirements. The Chief of the Prevention Division in each Coast Guard District Office makes this determination and requires that alternative compliance be as close as possible with the 72 COLREGS. These regulations set out the procedure by which a vessel may be certified for alternative compliance. The information collection and recordkeeping requirements in §§81.5 and 81.18 have been approved by the Office of Management and Budget under OMB control No. 1625-0019

## §81.5 Application for a Certificate of Alternative Compliance.

(a) The owner, builder, operator, or agent of a vessel of special construction or purpose who believes the vessel cannot fully comply with the 72 COLREGS light, shape, or sound signal provisions without interference with its special function may apply for a determination that alternative compliance is justified. The application must be in writing, submitted to the Chief of the Prevention Division of the Coast Guard District in which the vessel is being built or operated, and include the following information:
    (1) The name, address, and telephone number of the applicant.
    (2) The identification of the vessel by its:
        (i) Official number;
        (ii) Shipyard hull number;
        (iii) Hull identification number; or
        (iv) State number, if the vessel does not have an official number or hull identification number.
    (3) Vessel name and home port, if known.
    (4) A description of the vessel's area of operation.
    (5) A description of the provision for which the Certificate of Alternative Compliance is sought, including:
        (i) The 72 COLREGS Rule or Annex section number for which the Certificate of Alternative Compliance is sought;
        (ii) A description of the special function of the vessel that would be interfered with by full compliance with the provision of that Rule or Annex section; and
        (iii) A statement of how full compliance would interfere with the special function of the vessel.
    (6) A description of the alternative installation that is in closest possible compliance with the applicable 72 COLREGS Rule or Annex section.
    (7) A copy of the vessel's plans or an accurate scale drawing that clearly shows:
        (i) The required installation of the equipment under the 72 COLREGS,
        (ii) The proposed installation of the equipment for which certification is being sought, and
        (iii) Any obstructions that may interfere with the equipment when installed in:
            (A) The required location; and
            (B) The proposed location.

(b) The Coast Guard may request from the applicant additional information concerning the application.

## §81.9 Certificate of Alternative Compliance: Contents.

The Chief of the Prevention Division issues the Certificate of Alternative Compliance to the vessel based on a determination that it cannot comply fully with 72 COLREGS light, shape, and sound signal provisions without interference with its special function. This Certificate includes—

(a) Identification of the vessel as supplied in the application under §81.5(a)(2);

(b) The provision of the 72 COLREGS for which the Certificate authorizes alternative compliance;

(c) A certification that the vessel is unable to comply fully with the 72 COLREGS lights, shape, and sound signal requirements without interference with its special function;

(d) A statement of why full compliance would interfere with the special function of the vessel;

(e) The required alternative installation;

(f) A statement that the required alternative installation is in the closest possible compliance with the 72 COLREGS without interfering with the special function of the vessel;

(g) The date of issuance;

(h) A statement that the Certificate of Alternative Compliance terminates when the vessel ceases to be usually engaged in the operation for which the certificate is issued.


## §81.17 Certificate of Alternative Compliance: Termination.

The Certificate of Alternative Compliance terminates if the information supplied under §81.5(a) or the Certificate issued under §81.9 is no longer applicable to the vessel.


## §81.18 Notice and record of certification of vessels of special construction or purpose.

(a) In accordance with 33 U.S.C. 1605(c), a notice is published in the Federal Register of the following:
    (1) Each Certificate of Alternative Compliance issued under §81.9; and
    (2) Each Coast Guard vessel determined by the Commandant to be a vessel of special construction or purpose.

(b) Copies of Certificate of Alternative Compliance and documentation concerning Coast Guard vessels are available for inspection at Marine Transportation Systems Directorate, U.S. Coast Guard Headquarters, (CG-5PW), Stop 7509, 2703 Martin Luther King Avenue SE., Washington, DC 20593-7509.

(c) The owner or operator of a vessel issued a Certificate shall ensure that the vessel does not operate unless the Certificate of Alternative Compliance or a certified copy of that Certificate is on board the vessel and available for inspection by Coast Guard personnel.

## §81.20 Lights and sound signal appliances.

Each vessel under the 72 COLREGS, except the vessels of the Navy, is exempt from the requirements of the 72 COLREGS to the limitation for the period of time stated in Rule 38 (a), (b), (c), (d), (e), (f), and (g) if:

(a) Her keel is laid or is at a corresponding stage of construction before July 15, 1977; and

(b) She meets the International Regulations for Preventing Collisions at Sea, 1960 (77 Stat. 194, 33 U.S.C. 1051-1094).

# Part 89—INLAND NAVIGATION RULES: IMPLEMENTING RULES

## Subpart A—Certificate of Alternative Compliance

## §89.1 Definitions.

As used in this subpart:

Inland Rules refers to the Inland Navigation Rules contained in the Inland Navigational Rules Act of 1980 (Pub. L. 96-591) and the technical annexes established under that act.

A vessel of special construction or purpose means a vessel designed or modified to perform a special function and whose arrangement is thereby made relatively inflexible.

Interference with the special function of the vessel occurs when installation or use of lights, shapes, or sound-signaling appliances under the Inland Rules prevents or significantly hinders the operation in which the vessel is usually engaged.

## §89.3 General.

Vessels of special construction or purpose which cannot fully comply with the light, shape, and sound signal provisions of the Inland Rules without interfering with their special function may instead meet alternative requirements. The Chief of the Prevention Division in each Coast Guard District Office makes this determination and requires that alternative compliance be as close as possible with the Inland Rules. These regulations set out the procedure by which a vessel may be certified for alternative compliance. The information collection and recordkeeping requirements in §§89.5 and 89.18 have been approved by the Office of Management and Budget under OMB control No. 1625-0019.

## §89.5 Application for a Certificate of Alternative Compliance.

(a) The owner, builder, operator, or agent of a vessel of special construction or purpose who believes the vessel cannot fully comply with the Inland Rules light, shape, or sound signal provisions without interference with its special function may apply for a determination that alternative compliance is justified. The application must be in writing, submitted to the Chief of the Prevention Division of the Coast Guard District in which the vessel is being built or operated, and include the following information:
    (1) The name, address, and telephone number of the applicant.
    (2) The identification of the vessel by its:
        (i) Official number;
        (ii) Shipyard hull number;
        (iii) Hull identification number; or
        (iv) State number, if the vessel does not have an official number or hull identification number.

## §89.5 Application for a Certificate of Alternative Compliance. CONTINUED

(3) Vessel name and home port, if known.

(4) A description of the vessel's area of operation.

(5) A description of the provision for which the Certificate of Alternative Compliance is sought, including:

(i) The Inland Rules Rule or Annex section number for which the Certificate of Alternative Compliance is sought;

(ii) A description of the special function of the vessel that would be interfered with by full compliance with the provision of that Rule or Annex section; and

(iii) A statement of how full compliance would interfere with the special function of the vessel.

(6) A description of the alternative installation that is in closest possible compliance with the applicable Inland Navigation Rules Rule or Annex section.

(7) A copy of the vessel's plans or an accurate scale drawing that clearly shows:

(i) The required installation of the equipment under the Inland Rules,

(ii) The proposed installation of the equipment for which certification is being sought, and

(iii) Any obstructions that may interfere with the equipment when installed in:

(A) The required location; and

(B) The proposed location.

(b) The Coast Guard may request from the applicant additional information concerning the application.

## §89.9 Certificate of Alternative Compliance: Contents.

The Chief of the Prevention Division issues the Certificate of Alternative Compliance to the vessel based on a determination that it cannot comply fully with Inland Rules light, shape, and sound signal provisions without interference with its special function. This Certificate includes:

(a) Identification of the vessel as supplied in the application under §89.5(a)(2);

(b) The provision of the Inland Rules for which the Certificate authorizes alternative compliance;

(c) A certification that the vessel is unable to comply fully with the Inland Rules light, shape, and sound signal requirements without interference with its special function;

(d) A statement of why full compliance would interfere with the special function of the vessel;

(e) The required alternative installation;

(f) A statement that the required alternative installation is in the closest possible compliance with the Inland Rules without interfering with the special function of the vessel;

(g) The date of issuance;

(h) A statement that the Certificate of Alternative Compliance terminates when the vessel ceases to be usually engaged in the operation for which the certificate is issued.

## §89.17 Certificate of Alternative Compliance: Termination.

The Certificate of Alternative Compliance terminates if the information supplied under §89.5(a) or the Certificate issued under §89.9 is no longer applicable to the vessel.

## §89.18 Record of certification of vessels of special construction or purpose.

(a) Copies of Certificates of Alternative Compliance and documentation concerning Coast Guard vessels are available for inspection at the offices of the Marine Transportation Systems Directorate, U.S. Coast Guard Headquarters (CG-5PW), Stop 7509, 2703 Martin Luther King Avenue SE., Washington, DC 20593-7509.

(b) The owner or operator of a vessel issued a Certificate shall ensure that the vessel does not operate unless the Certificate of Alternative Compliance or a certified copy of that Certificate is on board the vessel and available for inspection by Coast Guard personnel.

## Subpart B—Waters Upon Which Certain Inland Navigation Rules Apply

## §89.21 Purpose.

Inland Navigation Rules 9(a)(ii), 14(d), and 15(b) apply to the Great Lakes, and along with 24(i), apply on the "Western Rivers" as defined in Rule 3(1), and to additional specifically designated waters. The purpose of this Subpart is to specify those additional waters upon which Inland Navigation Rules 9(a)(ii), 14(d), 15(b), and 24(i) apply.

## §89.23 Definitions.

As used in this subpart:
Inland Rules refers to the Inland Navigation Rules contained in the Inland Navigational Rules Act of 1980 (Pub. L. 96-591, 33 U.S.C. 2001 et. seq.) and the technical annexes established under that Act.

## §89.25 Waters upon which Inland Rules 9(a)(ii), 14(d), and 15(b) apply.

Inland Rules 9(a)(ii), 14(d), and 15(b) apply on the Great Lakes, the Western Rivers, and the following specified waters:

(a) Tennessee-Tombigbee Waterway.

(b) Tombigbee River.

(c) Black Warrior River.

(d) Alabama River.

(e) Coosa River.

(f) Mobile River above the Cochrane Bridge at St. Louis Point.

(g) Flint River.

(h) Chattahoochee River.

(i) The Apalachicola River above its confluence with the Jackson River.

## §89.27 Waters upon which Inland Rule 24(j) applies.

(a) Inland Rule 24(j) applies on the Western Rivers and the specified waters listed in §89.25 (a) through (i).

(b) Inland Rule 24(j) applies on the Gulf Intracoastal Waterway from St. Marks, Florida, to the Rio Grande, Texas, including the Morgan City-Port Allen Alternate Route and the Galveston-Freeport Cutoff, except that a power-driven vessel pushing ahead or towing alongside shall exhibit the lights required by Inland Rule 24(c), while transiting within the following areas:

(1) St. Andrews Bay from the Hathaway Fixed Bridge at Mile 284.6 East of Harvey Locks (EHL) to the DuPont Fixed Bridge at Mile 295.4 EHL.

(2) Pensacola Bay, Santa Rosa Sound and Big Lagoon from the Light "10" off of Trout Point at Mile 176.9 EHL to the Pensacola Fixed Bridge at Mile 189.1 EHL.

(3) Mobile Bay and Bon Secour Bay from the Dauphin Island Causeway Fixed Bridge at Mile 127.7 EHL to Little Point Clear at Mile 140 EHL.

(4) Mississippi Sound from Grand Island Waterway Light "1" at Mile 53.8 EHL to Light "40" off the West Point of Dauphin Island at Mile 118.7 EHL.

(5) The Mississippi River at New Orleans, Mississippi River-Gulf Outlet Canal and the Inner Harbor Navigation Canal from the junction of the Harvey Canal and the Algiers Alternate Route at Mile 6.5 West of Harvey Locks (WHL) to the Michoud Canal at Mile 18 EHL.

(6) The Calcasieu River from the Calcasieu Lock at Mile 238.6 WHL to the Ellender Lift Bridge at Mile 243.6 WHL.

(7) The Sabine Neches Canal from mile 262.5 WHL to mile 291.5 WHL.

(8) Bolivar Roads from the Bolivar Assembling Basin at Mile 346 WHL to the Galveston Causeway Bridge at Mile 357.3 WHL.

(9) Freeport Harbor from Surfside Beach Fixed Bridge at Mile 393.8 WHL to the Bryan Beach Pontoon Bridge at Mile 397.6 WHL.

(10) Matagorda Ship Channel area of Matagorda Bay from Range "K" Front Light at Mile 468.7 WHL to the Port O'Connor Jetty at Mile 472.2 WHL.

(11) Corpus Christi Bay from Redfish Bay Day Beacon "55" at Mile 537.4 WHL when in the Gulf Intracoastal Waterway main route or from the north end of Lydia Ann Island Mile 531.1A when in the Gulf Intracoastal Waterway Alternate Route to Corpus Christi Bay LT 76 at Mile 543.7 WHL.

(12) Port Isabel and Brownsville Ship Channel south of the Padre Island Causeway Fixed Bridge at Mile 665.1 WHL.

# Part 26—VESSEL BRIDGE-TO-BRIDGE RADIOTELEPHONE REGULATIONS

## §26.01 Purpose.

(a) The purpose of this part is to implement the provisions of the Vessel Bridge-to-Bridge Radiotelephone Act. This part:

(1) Requires the use of the vessel bridge-to-bridge radiotelephone;

(2) Provides the Coast Guard's interpretation of the meaning of important terms in the Act;

(3) Prescribes the procedures for applying for an exemption from the Act and the regulations issued under the Act and a listing of exemptions.

(b) Nothing in this part relieves any person from the obligation of complying with the rules of the road and the applicable pilot rules.

## §26.02 Definitions.

For the purpose of this part and interpreting the Act:

*Act* means the "Vessel Bridge-to-Bridge Radiotelephone Act", 33 U.S.C. sections 1201-1208;

*Length* is measured from end to end over the deck excluding sheer;

*Power-driven vessel* means any vessel propelled by machinery; and

*Secretary* means the Secretary of the Department in which the Coast Guard is operating;

*Territorial sea* means all waters as defined in §2.22(a)(1) of this chapter.

*Towing vessel* means any commercial vessel engaged in towing another vessel astern, alongside, or by pushing ahead.

*Vessel Traffic Services (VTS)* means a service implemented under Part 161 of this chapter by the United States Coast Guard designed to improve the safety and efficiency of vessel traffic and to protect the environment. The VTS has the capability to interact with marine traffic and respond to traffic situations developing in the VTS area.

*Vessel Traffic Service Area or VTS Area* means the geographical area encompassing a specific VTS area of service as described in Part 161 of this chapter. This area of service may be subdivided into sectors for the purpose of allocating responsibility to individual Vessel Traffic Centers or to identify different operating requirements.

Note: Although regulatory jurisdiction is limited to the navigable waters of the United States, certain vessels will be encouraged or may be required, as a condition of port entry, to report beyond this area to facilitate traffic management within the VTS area.

## §26.03 Radiotelephone required.

(a) Unless an exemption is granted under §26.09 and except as provided in paragraph (a)(4) of this section, this part applies to:

(1) Every power-driven vessel of 20 meters or over in length while navigating;

(2) Every vessel of 100 gross tons and upward carrying one or more passengers for hire while navigating;

(3) Every towing vessel of 26 feet or over in length while navigating; and

(4) Every dredge and floating plant engaged in or near a channel or fairway in operations likely to restrict or affect navigation of other vessels except for an unmanned or intermittently manned floating plant under the control of a dredge

## §26.03 Radiotelephone required. CONTINUED

(b) Every vessel, dredge, or floating plant described in paragraph (a) of this section must have a radiotelephone on board capable of operation from its navigational bridge, or in the case of a dredge, from its main control station, and capable of transmitting and receiving on the frequency or frequencies within the 156-162 Mega-Hertz band using the classes of emissions designated by the Federal Communications Commission for the exchange of navigational information.

(c) The radiotelephone required by paragraph (b) of this section must be carried on board the described vessels, dredges, and floating plants upon the navigable waters of the United States.

(d) The radiotelephone required by paragraph (b) of this section must be capable of transmitting and receiving on VHF FM channel 22A (157.1 MHz).

(e) While transiting any of the following waters, each vessel described in paragraph (a) of this section also must have on board a radiotelephone capable of transmitting and receiving on VHF FM channel 67 (156.375 MHz):
    (1) The lower Mississippi River from the territorial sea boundary, and within either the Southwest Pass safety fairway or the South Pass safety fairway specified in 33 CFR 166.200, to mile 242.4 AHP (Above Head of Passes) near Baton Rouge;
    (2) The Mississippi River-Gulf Outlet from the territorial sea boundary, and within the Mississippi River-Gulf outlet Safety Fairway specified in 33 CFR 166.200, to that channel's junction with the Inner Harbor Navigation Canal; and
    (3) The full length of the Inner Harbor Navigation Canal from its junction with the Mississippi River to that canal's entry to Lake Pontchartrain at the New Seabrook vehicular bridge.

(f) In addition to the radiotelephone required by paragraph (b) of this section, each vessel described in paragraph (a) of this section while transiting any waters within a Vessel Traffic Service Area, must have on board a radiotelephone capable of transmitting and receiving on the VTS designated frequency in Table 161.12(c) (VTS and VMRS Centers, Call Signs/MMSI, Designated Frequencies, and Monitoring Areas).

Note: A single VHF-FM radio capable of scanning or sequential monitoring (often referred to as "dual watch" capability) will not meet the requirements for two radios.

## §26.04 Use of the designated frequency.

(a) No person may use the frequency designated by the Federal Communications Commission under section 8 of the Act, 33 U.S.C. 1207(a), to transmit any information other than information necessary for the safe navigation of vessels or necessary tests.

(b) Each person who is required to maintain a listening watch under section 5 of the Act shall, when necessary, transmit and confirm, on the designated frequency, the intentions of his vessel and any other information necessary for the safe navigation of vessels.

(c) Nothing in these regulations may be construed as prohibiting the use of the designated frequency to communicate with shore stations to obtain or furnish information necessary for the safe navigation of vessels.

(d) On the navigable waters of the United States, channel 13 (156.65 MHz) is the designated frequency required to be monitored in accordance with §26.05(a) except that in the area prescribed in §26.03(e), channel 67 (156.375 MHz) is the designated frequency.

(e) On those navigable waters of the United States within a VTS area, the designated VTS frequency is an additional designated frequency required to be monitored in accordance with §26.05.

## §26.05 Use of radiotelephone.

Section 5 of the Act states that the radiotelephone required by this Act is for the exclusive use of the master or person in charge of the vessel, or the person designated by the master or person in charge to pilot or direct the movement of the vessel, who shall maintain a listening watch on the designated frequency. Nothing herein shall be interpreted as precluding the use of portable radiotelephone equipment to satisfy the requirements of this act.

## §26.06 Maintenance of radiotelephone; failure of radiotelephone.

Section 6 of the Act states:
(a) Whenever radiotelephone capability is required by this Act, a vessel's radiotelephone equipment shall be maintained in effective operating condition. If the radiotelephone equipment carried aboard a vessel ceases to operate, the master shall exercise due diligence to restore it or cause it to be restored to effective operating condition at the earliest practicable time. The failure of a vessel's radiotelephone equipment shall not, in itself, constitute a violation of this Act, nor shall it obligate the master of any vessel to moor or anchor his vessel; however, the loss of radiotelephone capability shall be given consideration in the navigation of the vessel.

## §26.07 Communications.

No person may use the services of, and no person may serve as, a person required to maintain a listening watch under section 5 of the Act, 33 U.S.C. 1204, unless the person can communicate in the English language.

## §26.08 Exemption procedures.

(a) The Commandant has redelegated to the Assistant Commandant for Prevention Policy, U.S. Coast Guard Headquarters, with the reservation that this authority shall not be further redelegated, the authority to grant exemptions from provisions of the Vessel Bridge-to-Bridge Radiotelephone Act and this part.

(b) Any person may petition for an exemption from any provision of the Act or this part;

(c) Each petition must be submitted in writing to Commandant (CG-DCO-D), Attn: Deputy for Operations Policy and Capabilities, U.S. Coast Guard Stop 7318,     2703 Martin Luther King Jr. Avenue SE., Washington, DC 20593-7318, and must state:
    (1) The provisions of the Act or this part from which an exemption is requested; and
    (2) The reasons why marine navigation will not be adversely affected if the exemption is granted and if the exemption relates to a local communication system how that system would fully comply with the intent of the concept of the Act but would not conform in detail if the exemption is granted.

## §26.09 List of exemptions.

(a) All vessels navigating on those waters governed by the navigation rules for Great Lakes and their connecting and tributary waters (33 U.S.C. 241 et seq.) are exempt from the requirements of the Vessel Bridge-to-Bridge Radiotelephone Act and this part until May 6, 1975.

(b) Each vessel navigating on the Great Lakes as defined in the Inland Navigational Rules Act of 1980 (33 U.S.C. 2001 et seq.) and to which the Vessel Bridge-to- Bridge Radiotelephone Act (33 U.S.C. 1201-1208) applies is exempt from the requirements in 33 U.S.C. 1203, 1204, and 1205 and the regulations under §§26.03, 26.04, 26.05, 26.06, and 26.07. Each of these vessels and each person to whom 33 U.S.C. 1208(a) applies must comply with Articles VII, X, XI, XII, XIII, XV, and XVI and Technical Regulations 1-9 of "The Agreement Between the United States of America and Canada for Promotion of Safety on the Great Lakes by Means of Radio, 1973."

# Notes

# U.S. AIDS TO NAVIGATION SYSTEM
## on navigable waters except Western Rivers

## LATERAL SYSTEM AS SEEN ENTERING FROM SEAWARD

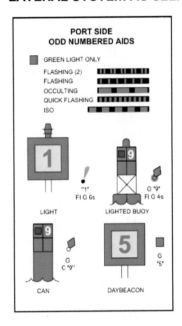

**PORT SIDE**
**ODD NUMBERED AIDS**

GREEN LIGHT ONLY

FLASHING (2)
FLASHING
OCCULTING
QUICK FLASHING
ISO

"1"
Fl G 6s
LIGHT

G "9"
Fl G 4s
LIGHTED BUOY

G
C "9"
CAN

G
"5"
DAYBEACON

**PREFERRED CHANNEL**
**NO NUMBERS - MAY BE LETTERED**

PREFERRED
CHANNEL TO
STARBOARD
TOPMOST BAND
GREEN

GREEN LIGHT ONLY

COMPOSITE GROUP FLASHING (2+1)

GR "A"
Fl (2+1) G 6s

GR
"U"

GR
C "S"
CAN

**PREFERRED CHANNEL**
**NO NUMBERS - MAY BE LETTERED**

PREFERRED
CHANNEL TO
PORT
TOPMOST BAND
RED

RED LIGHT ONLY

COMPOSITE GROUP FLASHING (2+1)

RG "B"
Fl (2+1) R 6s

RG
N "C"
NUN

RG
"G"

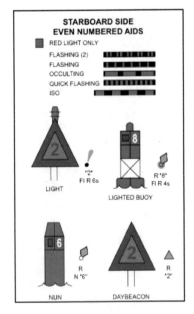

**STARBOARD SIDE**
**EVEN NUMBERED AIDS**

RED LIGHT ONLY

FLASHING (2)
FLASHING
OCCULTING
QUICK FLASHING
ISO

"2"
Fl R 6s
LIGHT

R "8"
Fl R 4s
LIGHTED BUOY

R
N "6"
NUN

R
"2"
DAYBEACON

# AIDS TO NAVIGATION HAVING NO LATERAL SIGNIFICANCE

### SAFE WATER
### NO NUMBERS - MAY BE LETTERED

☐ WHITE LIGHT ONLY    MORSE CODE

Mo (A)

RW "N"
Mo (A)

LIGHTED
AND/OR SOUND

RW "A"

MR

RW SP "B"

SPHERICAL

RW "N"

UNLIGHTED
AND/OR SOUND

## RANGE DAYBOARDS—MAY BE LETTERED

| KGW | KWG | KWB | KBW | KWR | KRW | KRB | KBR | KGB | KBG | KGR | KRG |

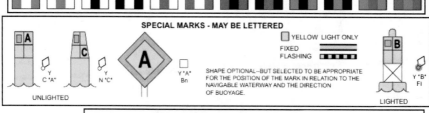

### SPECIAL MARKS - MAY BE LETTERED

☐ YELLOW LIGHT ONLY

FIXED
FLASHING

SHAPE OPTIONAL--BUT SELECTED TO BE APPROPRIATE
FOR THE POSITION OF THE MARK IN RELATION TO THE
NAVIGABLE WATERWAY AND THE DIRECTION
OF BUOYAGE.

A
C "A"  Y

C
N "C"  Y

A
Y "A"
Bn

B
Y "B"
Fl

UNLIGHTED

LIGHTED

## TYPICAL INFORMATION AND REGULATORY MARKS

INFORMATION AND REGULATORY MARKERS

WHEN LIGHTED, INFORMATION AND REGULATORY
MARKS MAY DISPLAY ANY WHITE LIGHT RHYTHM
EXCEPT QUICK FLASHING, Mo(A), AND FLASHING (2)

NW
☐ W
Bn    ◇ DANGER ◇

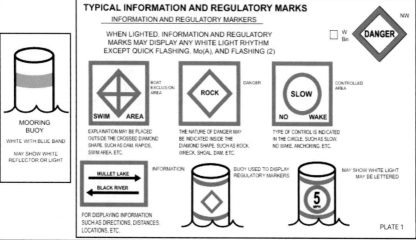

MOORING
BUOY

WHITE WITH BLUE BAND

MAY SHOW WHITE
REFLECTOR OR LIGHT

SWIM AREA

BOAT
EXCLUSION
AREA

EXPLANATION MAY BE PLACED
OUTSIDE THE CROSSED DIAMOND
SHAPE, SUCH AS DAM, RAPIDS,
SWIM AREA, ETC.

ROCK

DANGER

THE NATURE OF DANGER MAY
BE INDICATED INSIDE THE
DIAMOND SHAPE, SUCH AS ROCK,
WRECK, SHOAL, DAM, ETC.

SLOW
NO    WAKE

CONTROLLED
AREA

TYPE OF CONTROL IS INDICATED
IN THE CIRCLE, SUCH AS SLOW,
NO WAKE, ANCHORING, ETC.

MULLET LAKE
BLACK RIVER

INFORMATION

FOR DISPLAYING INFORMATION
SUCH AS DIRECTIONS, DISTANCES,
LOCATIONS, ETC.

BUOY USED TO DISPLAY
REGULATORY MARKERS

◇

5
MPH

MAY SHOW WHITE LIGHT
MAY BE LETTERED

PLATE 1

### DAYBOARDS - MAY BE LETTERED

☐ WHITE LIGHT ONLY

NR

☐ RW
Bn

NG

☐ GW
Bn

NB
M

☐ BW
Bn

Aids to Navigation marking the Intracoastal Waterway (ICW)
display unique yellow symbols to distinguish them from aids
marking other waters. Yellow triangles △ indicate aids should
be passed by keeping them on the starboard (right) hand of
the vessel. Yellow squares ☐ indicate aids should be passed
by keeping them on the port (left) hand of the vessel. A yellow
horizontal band ▭ provides no lateral information, but simply
identifies aids as marking the ICW

### ISOLATED DANGER
### NO NUMBERS - MAY BE LETTERED

☐ WHITE LIGHT ONLY

Fl (2) 5s

A

BR "A"
Fl (2) 5s

C

BR "C"

LIGHTED

UNLIGHTED

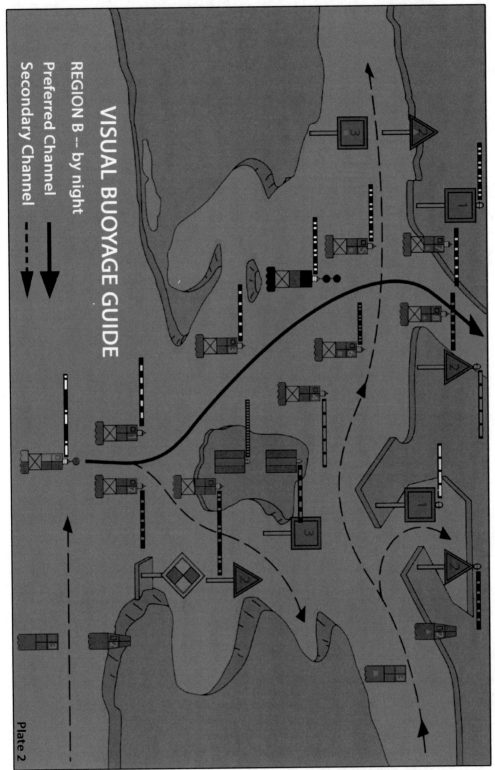

## VISUAL BUOYAGE GUIDE

REGION B – by night

Preferred Channel

Secondary Channel

Plate 2

## VISUAL BUOYAGE GUIDE

REGION B -- by day

Preferred Channel

Secondary Channel

# U.S. AIDS TO NAVIGATION SYSTEM
## on the Western River System

## AS SEEN ENTERING FROM SEAWARD

PORT SIDE
OR RIGHT DESCENDING BANK

GREEN OR ☐ WHITE LIGHTS (CROSSING)

FLASHING
ISO

LIGHT     CAN     LIGHTED BUOY

SG     CG

PASSING DAYMARK     CROSSING DAYMARK

176.9
MILE BOARD

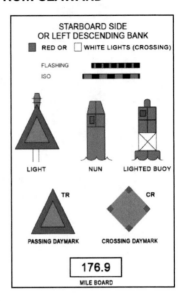

STARBOARD SIDE
OR LEFT DESCENDING BANK

RED OR ☐ WHITE LIGHTS (CROSSING)

FLASHING
ISO

LIGHT     NUN     LIGHTED BUOY

TR     CR

PASSING DAYMARK     CROSSING DAYMARK

176.9
MILE BOARD

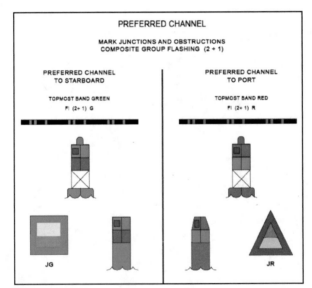

PREFERRED CHANNEL

MARK JUNCTIONS AND OBSTRUCTIONS
COMPOSITE GROUP FLASHING (2 + 1)

PREFERRED CHANNEL
TO STARBOARD

TOPMOST BAND GREEN

Fl (2+ 1) G

JG

PREFERRED CHANNEL
TO PORT

TOPMOST BAND RED

Fl (2+ 1) R

JR

### DAYMARKS HAVING NO LATERAL SIGNIFICANCE

MAY BE LETTERED

□ WHITE LIGHT ONLY

NR · NG · NB

UNLIGHTED

A · C · NY · B

□ YELLOW LIGHT ONLY
FIXED
FLASHING

LIGHTED

### RANGE DAYMARKS - MAY BE LETTERED

INFORMATION AND REGULATORY MARKS
WHEN LIGHTED, INFORMATION AND REGULATORY
MARKS MAY DISPLAY ANY LIGHT RHYTHM EXCEPT
QUICK FLASHING AND FLASHING (2).

□ WHITE LIGHT ONLY

EXCLUSION AREA · RESTRICTED OPERATIONS · DANGER · NW DANGER

# UNIFORM STATE WATERWAY MARKING SYSTEM

## STATE WATERS AND DESIGNATED WATERS FOR PRIVATE AIDS TO NAVIGATION

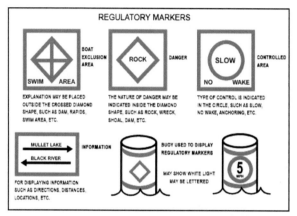

### REGULATORY MARKERS

SWIM AREA — BOAT EXCLUSION AREA

ROCK — DANGER

SLOW NO WAKE — CONTROLLED AREA

EXPLANATION MAY BE PLACED OUTSIDE THE CROSSED DIAMOND SHAPE, SUCH AS DAM, RAPIDS, SWIM AREA, ETC.

THE NATURE OF DANGER MAY BE INDICATED INSIDE THE DIAMOND SHAPE, SUCH AS ROCK, WRECK, SHOAL, DAM, ETC.

TYPE OF CONTROL IS INDICATED IN THE CIRCLE, SUCH AS SLOW, NO WAKE, ANCHORING, ETC.

MULLET LAKE / BLACK RIVER — INFORMATION

FOR DISPLAYING INFORMATION SUCH AS DIRECTIONS, DISTANCES, LOCATIONS, ETC.

BUOY USED TO DISPLAY REGULATORY MARKERS

MAY SHOW WHITE LIGHT
MAY BE LETTERED

5 MPH

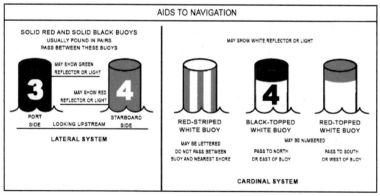

### AIDS TO NAVIGATION

SOLID RED AND SOLID BLACK BUOYS
USUALLY FOUND IN PAIRS
PASS BETWEEN THESE BUOYS

MAY SHOW GREEN REFLECTOR OR LIGHT

3

MAY SHOW RED REFLECTOR OR LIGHT

4

PORT SIDE — LOOKING UPSTREAM — STARBOARD SIDE

LATERAL SYSTEM

MAY SHOW WHITE REFLECTOR OR LIGHT

RED-STRIPED WHITE BUOY

MAY BE LETTERED
DO NOT PASS BETWEEN BUOY AND NEAREST SHORE

BLACK-TOPPED WHITE BUOY

4

MAY BE NUMBERED

PASS TO NORTH OR EAST OF BUOY

RED-TOPPED WHITE BUOY

PASS TO SOUTH OR WEST OF BUOY

CARDINAL SYSTEM

WHITE WITH BLUE BAND
MAY SHOW WHITE REFLECTOR OR LIGHT

MOORING BUOY

Plate 4

# FICTITIOUS NAUTICAL CHART

Plate 3

# U.S. COAST GUARD

# U.S. AIDS TO NAVIGATION SYSTEM

*What You Need to Know About the Markers on the Water*

*A Handy Guide from the United States Coast Guard*

# INTRODUCTION

**AIDS TO NAVIGATION ARE THE WATERWAYS' ROAD SIGNS**

Aids to Navigation can provide a boater with information similar to that which drivers get from street signs, stop signals, road barriers, detours, and traffic lights.

This booklet will give you, the recreational boater, the basic information you need about the U.S. Aids to Navigation System (USATONS). This information will help you recognize, understand, and navigate by the colors, shapes, numbers, and lights you will encounter on the water. It will also give you the basic tools you need to read a nautical chart. In addition, you will find information on safety, the proper way to interact with other vessels, tips on boating at night, and how to handle special situations you might encounter, like bridges and locks.

Take some time to review this booklet, and keep it onboard your boat as a quick reference. Your understanding of the markers you see on the water will help ensure that you, your family, and your friends have fun - and safe - boating trips.

Best Regards,

United States Coast Guard Boating Safety Division

*Most boating accidents are preventable! Be sure to:*

**BOAT** *Responsibly*

- *Always wear your life jacket and require the same of your passengers*
- *Never boat under the influence*
- *Take a boating safety course*
- *Get a free Vessel Safety Check*

# 1. NAVIGATION RULES *(RULES OF THE ROAD)*

Boaters call navigation rules - the basic laws governing the steering or sailing of a boat - "The Rules of the Road." The Rules of the Road define the roles and responsibilities of vessel operators. If all operators obeyed these rules, most accidents could be avoided.

One of the reasons the Rules of the Road exist is to keep boats from colliding with each other and with other objects. Since collisions are the number one type of accident on the water, boaters should remember the following Rules of the Road.

*The Rules vary slightly depending on whether you are boating on inland or on international waters. As an example, when operating on inland waters, sound signals are signals of* **intent**; *when operating on international waters, they are signals of* **action**.

*Post a lookout.* Designate someone to watch for dangers that may come from any direction.

*Maintain a safe speed.* Except where speed is restricted by regulation or the waterway is marked by a "No Wake" or "Slow Speed" Aid, you must judge "safe speed" for yourself, taking into account visibility, vessel traffic, your boat's ability to maneuver, and the weather conditions.

*Avoid a collision.* The Rules of the Road include the actions to take when encountering another vessel on the water. Some of the most common situations you may encounter are: overtaking, meeting head on, and crossing the bow of another vessel. In each case, the boat designated as the "give-way" vessel is required to yield to the other boat, while the boat designated as the "stand-on" vessel should maintain its course and speed.

## Overtaking Situation (Navigation Rule 13)

*Action(s):* The give-way vessel (bottom) can pass on either side of the stand-on vessel (top).

*Sound signals, inland:* Passing portside requires two short (1-second) blasts on the horn signaling the overtaking boat's intention, and two short blasts for the stand-on vessel's agreement. Passing to starboard requires one short blast for intent and agreement.

*Sound signals, international:* Passing portside requires two prolonged (4-6 seconds) and two short blasts for the overtaking boat's intention, two short blasts for the stand-on vessel's agreement. Passing to starboard requires two prolonged and one short blast for intention. An agreement signal is only required when operating in a narrow channel or fairway; then the following blast pattern signals your agreement: one prolonged/one short/one prolonged/one short.

## Head-On Situation (Navigation Rule 14)

*Port-to-Port Passing (preferred)*

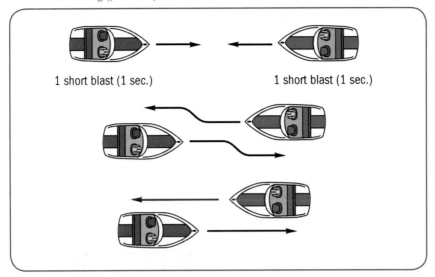

1 short blast (1 sec.)    1 short blast (1 sec.)

*Starboard-to-Starboard Passing*

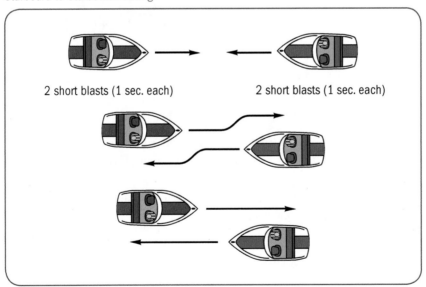

2 short blasts (1 sec. each)    2 short blasts (1 sec. each)

*Action(s):* When meeting another vessel head on, a port-to-port passing is preferred. Passing starboard-to-starboard is acceptable when necessary.

*Sound signals:* Passing port-to-port requires one short horn blast to signal intention and one short blast for agreement. Passing to starboard requires two short blasts from each vessel.

### Crossing Situation (Navigation Rule 15)

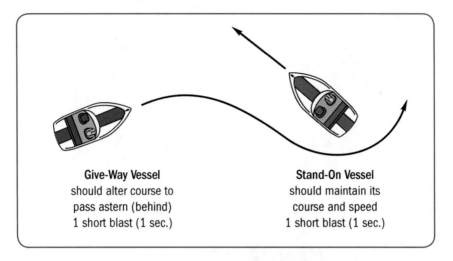

**Give-Way Vessel**
should alter course to
pass astern (behind)
1 short blast (1 sec.)

**Stand-On Vessel**
should maintain its
course and speed
1 short blast (1 sec.)

*Action(s):* In a crossing situation, the give-way vessel must act to avoid a collision. This may include altering its course to pass astern of the stand-on vessel or slowing down. The stand-on vessel should maintain its course and speed.

*Sound signals, inland:* The give-way vessel signals the stand-on vessel with one short horn blast. The stand-on vessel agrees with one short horn blast.

*Sound signals, international:* The give-way vessel signals the stand-on vessel with one short horn blast. No agreement signal by the stand-on vessel is required.

**When meeting another boat, make early and substantial changes to your course. This helps the other operator understand your intentions.**

◇ **INFO** ◇
*There is much more to the Navigation Rules than can be covered here. For more information, go to www.uscgboating.org or www.navcen.uscg.gov.*

## 2. THE ESSENTIAL MARKERS: On the Water and On the Charts

The two main types of Aids to Navigation are buoys and beacons.

*Buoys* are Aids that float on top of the water, but are moored to the bottom of the body of water. Some have a light affixed to the top; some do not. A buoy with a cylindrical shape and a conical top is referred to as a "nun." A buoy with a cylindrical shape and a flat top is called a "can."

*Beacons* are Aids that are permanently fixed, most commonly to the bottom of a body of water. A beacon that has a light attached is simply referred to as a "light"; a beacon without a light attached is called a "daybeacon."

Both buoys and beacons can provide a variety of navigation information via shape, color, light, and/or audible signal.

*Dayboards* are informational signboards. The term *topmark* refers to a non-lighting element, such as a sphere, that may be affixed to the top of an Aid.

RED LIGHTED BUOY

R "4"
QR

GREEN CAN BUOY

G
C "5A"

RED/GREEN NUN BUOY

RG
N "CF"

RED LIGHT

Fl R 4s
30ft 6M "4"

Red: always even numbers

GREEN LIGHT

Fl G 4s 15ft 5M "5"

Green: always odd numbers

RED DAYBEACON

R "2A"

## Understanding the Symbols in This Booklet

Buoys, beacons, and all other Aids have a corresponding symbol used on nautical charts. In this booklet, you will see representations of Aids, each alongside its nautical chart symbol:

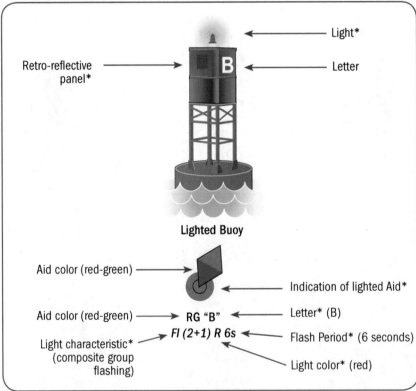

\* Not on all Aids

## Nautical Charts

It is critical to know where you are going, what routes to take, and which areas to avoid before you begin your boating trip. Nautical charts are the boating equivalent of road maps. A nautical chart provides boaters with an aerial view of a waterway with its Aids to Navigation, landmarks, and bridges, as well as information on water depth, latitude and longitude, and a variety of other important navigational information.

· *Always use a current navigation chart and be sure to check www.navcen.uscg.gov for any relevant Notices to Mariners before your trip.*

· *While electronic chart systems (ECS) can provide boaters with excellent information, keep relevant paper charts on board. Should your ECS or GPS malfunction, you will be very glad to have a backup.*

· *Remember that most accidents are caused by human error. Do not let an electronic navigation device take the place of knowing and adhering to the Navigation Rules.*

## What You See Depends on Where You Boat

The Aids to Navigation system used on the majority of American waterways is referred to as the U.S. Aids to Navigation System or IALA-B. A description of USATONS follows.

The Mississippi River and its tributaries follow a variation of USATONS called the Western Rivers Marking System. An explanation of this system begins on page 23.

The system used exclusively on the Intracoastal Waterway, which runs along the United States coast from New Jersey through Texas, is described beginning on page 25.

Another system, called the Uniform State Waterway Marking System, has mostly been phased out. However, these Aids are shown on page 26 as you may occasionally encounter them.

*There are also private Aids to Navigation, which are Aids that are neither owned nor maintained by the U.S. Coast Guard. These typically look similar to those in the systems described in this booklet and are represented by the same nautical chart symbols, with the addition of "Priv," or "Priv maintd."*

## 3. U.S. AIDS TO NAVIGATION SYSTEM *(IALA-B)*

### Lateral Aids to Navigation

Lateral Aids to Navigation are generally used for well-defined channels to indicate the route to be followed. These Aids show the sides of a navigable channel, mark junctions and forks or splits in the channel, indicate the safe side to pass a hazard to navigation, and mark the safe centerline on wide bodies of water.

They are used in conjunction with a conventional direction of buoyage (a local direction of buoyage when approaching a harbor, river estuary, or other waterway from seaward).

### *"Red, Right, Returning"*

You may have heard the phrase, "Red, Right, Returning." This expression refers to the fact that when returning (entering a channel from the open sea or proceeding upstream), a boater must keep the red Aids on the right (starboard) side of the boat. These Aids have even numbers, and the numbers should increase as you proceed inland.

When proceeding toward open water (seaward), navigate so that the green Aids are to starboard. In this instance, you will see odd numbers on the Aids and the numbers should decrease as you proceed toward open water (seaward).

If there is no route marked, navigate clockwise around landmasses.

## Proceeding Upstream

### Green Aids: Odd Numbers

Square dayboards, buoys, and cans

| | |
|---|---|
| G "7" | Daybeacon |
| "5" Fl G 6s | Light |
| G C "3" | Can |
| G "1" Fl G 4s | Lighted Buoy |

### Red Aids: Even Numbers

Red, Right, Returning: when proceeding upstream, keep the red Aids to starboard

| | |
|---|---|
| Daybeacon | R "8" |
| Light | "6" Fl R 6s |
| Nun | R N "4" |
| Lighted Buoy | R "2" Fl R 4s |

**Open Water (seaward)**

### Characteristics

- Beacons may have green odd numbers.
- Buoys may have white odd numbers.
- If lit, the light will be green and is likely to flash in one of the following patterns:

Flashing (2)
Flashing
Occulting
Quick Flashing
Isophase

### Characteristics

- Beacons may have red even numbers.
- Buoys may have white even numbers.
- If lit, the light will be red and is likely to flash in one of the following patterns:

Flashing (2)
Flashing
Occulting
Quick Flashing
Isophase

*(see page 22 for more on lights)*

## Preferred-Channel Aids

Beacons and buoys that have horizontal bands of both red and green mark the junction of navigable channels. The top-most color indicates the direction of the preferred, or primary, channel.

When returning (entering a channel from the open sea or proceeding upstream), keeping the Aids with red as the top-most color on the right (starboard) side of the boat will place the boater in the preferred channel, while keeping those Aids on the port side will place the boater in the secondary channel. When proceeding toward open water (seaward), keeping the Aids with green as the top-most color on the right (starboard) side of the boat will place the boater in the preferred channel, while keeping those Aids on the port side will place the boater in the secondary channel.

| | | Preferred Channel | | |
|---|---|---|---|---|
| GR "U" | Daybeacon | | Daybeacon | RG "G" |
| GR C "S" | Can Buoy | | Nun Buoy | RG N "C" |
| GR "A" Fl (2+1) G 6s | Lighted Buoy | | Lighted Buoy | RG "B" Fl (2+1) R 6s |

*Characteristics*
· Green on top.
· Have a letter designation.
· Buoys will feature a white letter.
· If lit: ▮▮▮▮ COMPOSITE GROUP FLASHING (2+1)

*Characteristics*
· Red on top.
· Have a letter designation.
· Buoys will feature a white letter.
· If lit: ▮▮▮▮ COMPOSITE GROUP FLASHING (2+1)

*(see page 22 for more on lights)*

## Non-Lateral Aids to Navigation

Non-lateral Aids are the on-the-water versions of the informational, regulatory, and warning signs encountered on the road.

### *Diamond-Shaped Dayboards*

Diamond shaped dayboards are used to help determine location. They are the nautical equivalent of "You Are Here" markers. An appropriate nautical chart must be consulted to determine your exact position.

*Characteristics*
- White with red, green, or black diamonds.
- Usually lettered (the letter can be matched to a nautical chart to check position).
- In the illustrations above, "NR," "NG," and "NB" indicate non-lateral red, green, and black. The chart symbol is to the lower right of each illustration (e.g., "RW Bn" indicates a red-and-white beacon).

## Safe Water Marks

These Aids are used to mark fairways, mid-channels, and offshore approach points. They have unobstructed water on all sides. A buoy, lighted or unlighted, may show a red topmark. An appropriate nautical chart must be consulted to determine exact position.

## Isolated Danger Marks

These Aids indicate an isolated danger that may be passed on all sides. Use caution when approaching.

BR "A"
Fl (2) 5s

BR "C"

Lighted

Unlighted

*Characteristics*
- Buoy with black and red horizontal bands.
- May be lettered.
- Black double-sphere topmark.
- If lit: ▮▮ ▮▮ ▮▮ *Fl (2) 5s*

## Range Dayboards

These Aids, which are usually shore-mounted, come in pairs to help the vessel operator maintain a straight and safe course within a navigable channel. Each member of the pair is separated from the next in distance and elevation, with the one in front shorter than the one behind it. When the two appear to be vertically stacked, the vessel is on the range line.

*Side View*

Rear light

Front light

*Front View*

Left of range line

Right of range line

On range line

When the front (bottom) marker is to the right of the rear (top) one, you are to the left of the range. You should turn right (starboard) to get onto the range line.

When the front (bottom) marker is to the left of the rear (top) one, you are to the right of the range. You should turn left (port) to get onto the range line.

The two range markers are in line, which indicates you are on the range line.

Rear marker

Front marker

Rear marker

Front marker

Rear marker

Front marker

**INFO**

*The colors of range dayboards do not impact navigation – colors are simply chosen based on how well they stand out from the background scenery. Some combinations:*

KGW  KWG  KBW  KWB  KWR  KRW  KRB  KBR  KGB  KBG  KGR  KRG

*Characteristics*
- Rectangular with two colors arranged as three vertical stripes.
- May be lettered.
- When lit, rear light will be higher then the front light.
- Light characteristics may vary; usually the rear (upper) light remains lit (fixed), while the front (lower) light flashes.

Iso R 1

QR

## Information and Regulatory Marks

These orange-and-white Aids are used to alert vessel operators to various warnings and regulations.

| Symbol | Meaning | Examples |
|---|---|---|
| ◇ | **Danger**<br>A diamond shape alerts boaters to hazards | DANGER   ROCK |
| ○ | **Restricted Operations**<br>Marks with a circle indicate areas with regulated operations | NO WAKE / IDLE SPEED   5 mph |
| ⊕ | **Exclusion**<br>A diamond shape with a cross means boats are prohibited from the area | BOATS KEEP OUT   SWIM AREA |
| □ | **Information**<br>Marks with a square provide helpful information such as directions, distances, and locations | GAS DOCK   BOAT RAMP |

*Characteristics*

- White with an orange horizontal band at both top and bottom.
- Black text within or around an orange square, circle, or diamond; or black text outside a diamond with an orange cross.
- May be buoys or beacons.
- If lit, the light will be white and may have any light rhythm except quick flashing, flashing (2), or Morse code "A."
- The chart symbol for this type of buoy is: W Or

## Special Aids

These Aids indicate special areas or features such as anchoring, traffic separation, fishnet area, cables or pipelines, military exercise areas, and jetties.

Unlighted

Lighted

*Characteristics*
- All-yellow.
- Come in a variety of shapes.
- May have one black letter.
- If lit: ▬▬▬▬▬ or ▮▮▮▮▮▮▮▮▮▮▮

## State Waters Obstruction Mark

The State Water Obstruction Mark indicates to a vessel operator that an obstruction to navigation extends from the nearest shore to the buoy. Do not pass between the buoy and the shore.

*Characteristics*
- Black-and-white vertically striped buoy.
- May show a white reflector or display a quick-flashing white light.

## Mooring Buoys

While not a navigational Aid, mooring buoys are worth mentioning. They are the only type of buoys to which mooring is permitted. Most mooring buoys are privately owned or are rental buoys. Permission is usually needed to use them.

*Characteristics*
- White with blue horizontal band.
- Cylinder and sphere shapes.
- May show a white reflector or display white or yellow light.

## Visual Buoyage Guide Example
(fictitious)

**Preferred Channel**

**Secondary Channel**

**Intracoastal Waterway**

## Nautical Chart Example
(fictitious; same circumstances as above)

## 4. BOATING AT NIGHT

Boating at night can make even familiar waters unrecognizable. Visual depth perception is lessened and lights from the shore can be difficult to distinguish from those on the water. To make nighttime boating safer, keep the following in mind.

### Navigation Lights

Vessels are required to show navigation lights from sunset to sunrise and during periods of restricted visibility. Understanding these light displays will provide invaluable information to the boater, as these lights can help the boater determine the length of another

vessel, its orientation in relation to your boat, and the general direction in which it is headed. All operators must ensure that their vessel's navigation lights are working and that the positioning and distance from which they can be seen meet federal regulations.

It is important to know which navigation lights you will see from another boat in certain situations. This can help you determine if you are in an overtaking, meeting, or crossing situation. The following chart illustrates the navigation lights you will see from various angles:

| Starboard | Bow | Stern | Port Side |

---

**INFO**

*Whenever you see a red navigation light from another vessel, give way. It is the stand-on vessel. According to the Rules of the Road, it has the right of way (see page 2).*

*If you see both the red and green sidelights of another boat, it is coming straight toward you. You should take action to change course in order to avoid a collision.*

**Keep in Mind**

- It is risky to rely on memory or to take shortcuts at night. Stick to the main channel. Your best bet is to navigate by the appropriate chart and identify the corresponding Aids to Navigation.

- Make sure you are familiar with the handling characteristics of your boat so you can concentrate on interpreting the Aids to Navigation.

- Slow down. Distances are more difficult to judge at night and you will need more time to distinguish the various types of lights you will see: navigation lights, lights from Aids, and lights on shore.

- Listen. You might hear certain sounds before you see the related objects or situations that require you to change course, such as another boat's engine or sound signals, an Aid's bell or gong, or noises from shore. (Note that sound travels far over water.)

- Turn on your navigation lights from sunset to sunrise and during daytime periods of reduced visibility, such as rain and fog.

- Turn off any lights that might interfere with, or be confused with, navigation lights.

**Nighttime Buoyage Guide Example**
(fictitious; same circumstances as pages 17-18)

## Aids to Navigation at Night

At night, Aids to Navigation can only be identified by their light characteristics:

· Color (red ●, green ●, white ◯, or yellow ◯).

· Light display (sequence of flashes).

· Period (time it takes to go through one sequence of flashes).

· Equipped with retroreflective material.

The various combinations of these characteristics enable boaters to tell one Aid from another in darkness. The following shows how common light display characteristics are illustrated and how they operate:

| Illustration | Chart Abbreviation | Type/Description |
|---|---|---|
| ▭ | F | **Fixed** <br> Shines continuously and steadily; no dark phase. |
| ■■■■■■■ | Fl | **Flashing** <br> The light goes on at regular intervals; the duration of the light phases are less than the duration of the dark phases. |
| ■■ ■ ■ ■ ■■ | Fl (2) | **Group Flashing** <br> Groups of two flashes that are repeated several times a minute. |
| ■■ ■ ■ ■■ | Fl (2+1) | **Composite Group Flashing** <br> A group of two flashes followed by a single flash, the entirety repeated several times a minute. |
| ■ ■ ■ ■ | Iso | **Isophase** <br> All durations of light and dark are equal. |
| ■■ ■ ■■ ■ ■ | Mo (A) | **Morse Code** <br> Short ("dots") and long ("dashes") flashes of light are used to represent Morse code; usually flashes the letter "A." |
| ■ ■ ■ ■ | Oc | **Occulting** <br> The light goes on at regular intervals; the duration of the light phases is greater than the duration of the dark phases. |
| ■■■■■■■ | Q | **Quick (Flashing)** <br> Very rapid flashing (more than 60 flashes a minute). |

## 5. AIDS TO NAVIGATION SYSTEMS

### Western Rivers Marking System

When on the Mississippi River, tributaries above Baton Rouge, and several other rivers that flow toward the Gulf of Mexico, boaters must follow a system called the Western Rivers Marking System, a variation of the U.S. Aids to Navigation System.

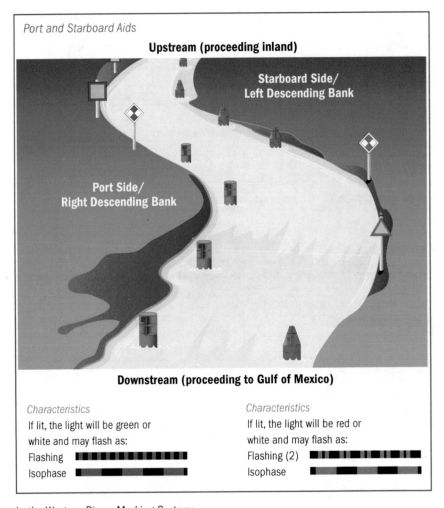

In the Western Rivers Marking System:

· Buoys are not numbered.

· Beacons are not numbered, but normally have a mile marker that indicates the distance in statute miles from a fixed point, typically the river's mouth.

- Crossing daybeacons are used to assist river traffic by indicating where the channel has changed from one side of the river to the other; the aid that marks this channel change will be on the opposite side of the river. When encountered, a vessel operator should head for the Aid, using its color as a channel mark.

- Isolated danger marks and safe-water marks are not used.

- River banks are named based on their downstream direction: either "left bank" and "right bank" or "left descending bank" and "right descending bank."

- Because of their somewhat temporary nature, Western River buoys do not have numbers or letters and are not always marked on river charts because they tend to drift due to fluctuating water level, current speed, and shifting shoals.

*Preferred-Channel Aids*

**Upstream**

Lighted buoy

Lighted buoy

Can

Nun

Daybeacon

**Downstream**

Daybeacon

*Characteristics*
If lit, the light will be green and will flash as:
Flashing
Fl (2+1) G

*Characteristics*
If lit, the light will be red and will flash as:
Flashing
Fl (2+1) R

## Intracoastal Waterway

The Intracoastal Waterway (ICW) runs just inland and parallel to the Atlantic and Gulf coasts from Manasquan, New Jersey to the Mexican border. The Aids to Navigation of the ICW closely resemble the green and red buoys and beacons of the lateral system previously discussed.

When operating in the ICW, the color of the Aids will typically correspond to the USATONS scheme (Red, Right, Returning). The yellow squares, triangles, and bands attached to the Aids are the primary ICW indicators. Boaters need to understand these markings to safely navigate the ICW. Some examples:

There are three types of symbols:

When following the ICW from New Jersey through Texas, keep yellow triangles △ on your starboard and yellow squares ☐ on your port, regardless of the color of the Aid on which they appear.

The yellow horizontal band [▭] reflector can be found on any non-lateral Aid. It simply identifies the Aid as marking the ICW.

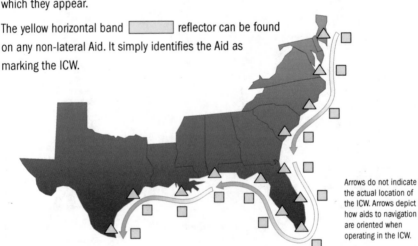

Arrows do not indicate the actual location of the ICW. Arrows depict how aids to navigation are oriented when operating in the ICW.

## Uniform State Waterway Marking System

The Uniform State Waterway Marking System (USWMS) was discontinued and replaced by the U.S. Aids to Navigation System (USATONS) in 2003. Should you come across one that has not yet been replaced, a guide is provided below:

*Lateral System – USWMS*

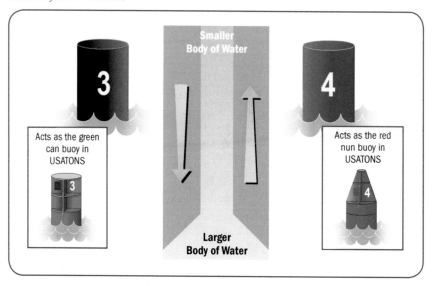

*Cardinal System – USWMS*

Cardinal buoys serve as the USWMS version of USATONS' preferred-channel markers, as they indicate the primary route. They are named "cardinal" buoys after the cardinal points (north, south, east, and west) of the compass:

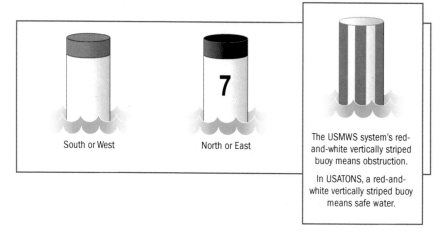

# 6. SPECIAL SITUATIONS

## Bridges

*Lighting Systems*

Bridges are lit to help boaters navigate under them from sunset to sunrise and during other periods of reduced visibility. In general, red lights indicate portions of the bridge where it is unsafe to attempt passage, and green lights indicate areas of safe passage. See key below.

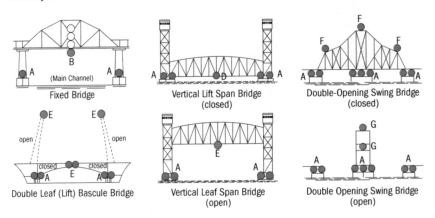

A ● – Piers and supports.

B ● – Centerline of navigable channel.

C ○ – Three white lights stacked vertically show the preferred route, if there is more than one navigable channel.

D ● – Used on some lift bridges to indicate the lift is closed.

E ● – Lift is open to vessel traffic.

F ● – Double-opening swing bridges show three red lights when closed.

G ● – Double-opening swing bridges show two green lights when open.

## Clearance Gauges

If it is not obvious whether or not there is enough vertical room to travel under a certain bridge, boaters should refer to its clearance gauge (affixed to the bridge's right side upon approach). This marks the distance between the "low steel" of the bridge channel span and the waterline, not the depth of the water under the bridge.

## Drawbridge-Opening Protocol

When passage under an open drawbridge is required, the boater must make a request of the drawbridge operator. The bridge tender will acknowledge the signal. The most common protocols are:

### VHF-FM

- Boaters may hail the drawbridge operator on channels 13 or 16. (Channel 9 should be used in Florida, Georgia, and South Carolina.)
- Always use the low-power output (1 watt) setting.

### Sound Signals

#### Approaching a Closed Draw

- An opening signal consists of one prolonged blast (4 to 6 seconds) and one short blast (1 second); this can be from a whistle, horn, megaphone, or hailer.
- The operator will reply with the prolonged-then-short blast if the draw will be opened immediately.
- Five short blasts in rapid succession mean that the operator cannot comply at that moment.

#### Approaching an Open Draw

- If the draw is already open, an opening signal (prolonged blast plus short blast) must be made.
- If no reply is received within 30 seconds, you may proceed with caution.
- Five short blasts in rapid succession mean that the operator must close the draw; do not proceed.

## Controlled-Access Areas

In order to ensure public safety and national security, the Coast Guard periodically establishes controlled-access areas that have special operational or navigational requirements. Safety Zones, Security Zones, and Regulated Navigation Areas might require reduced speed within a certain radius of a salvage operation, for example, or restrict access altogether near a high-profile event or a power plant. These areas should be avoided or approached with caution.

To make sure you know where the controlled-access areas are - and the specific parameters of each - always have the most current nautical chart and the latest Notices to Mariners before you head out (www.navcen.uscg.gov). Contact the local Coast Guard office or other law enforcement agency for specific details about such areas.

As a general rule, however, it is wise to avoid dams, power plants, and commercial port operation areas, especially those that involve the military, cruise lines, or petroleum facilities.

### Naval Vessel Protection Zones

A Naval Vessel Protection Zone is a permanent controlled-access area that surrounds every U.S. naval vessel. The parameters are clear: do not come closer than 100 yards of a vessel, and operate at minimum speed within 500 yards of the vessel. Violating a Naval Vessel Protection Zone is a felony offense with the possibility of a prison sentence and/or fines of up to $250,000.

**INFO** *If you feel you must enter a controlled-access area to ensure safe navigation, immediately contact the Coast Guard on VHF-FM Channel 16.*

### Locks

A lock is an engineered structure that enables vessels to move between waterways of differing heights. As when traveling under drawbridges, there are specific procedures in place for navigating through locks. Specifics may vary in certain regions, but in general:

- Stay between the red and green buoys that mark the river's navigable channel.
- Request an opening with a sound signal consisting of one prolonged blast (4 to 6 seconds) and one short blast (1 second) within one mile of the lock; this can be made by using the lock's pull-cord or your whistle, horn, megaphone, or hailer.

- Wait for the lock operator to signal you with horn blasts; additional signals may include traffic lights or flashing lights.

- Enter the lock at reduced speed.

- Make sure all passengers remain seated and wear their life jackets.

- Tie your craft to the mooring devices after entering; a minimum of 50 feet of line is recommended.

- Use fenders to avoid damage to your vessel and to lock walls.

- When through, wait for the lock operator's signal (horn and/or lights), then leave the lock at idle speed.

There is a specific order of lockage priority among vessels. Military and most commercial vessels have priority over recreational vessels.

### Low-Head Dams

Low-head dams have been built to raise the level of rivers or streams for various reasons. They can be extremely dangerous to small boats and swimmers; so much so, they have been nicknamed "drowning machines."

Small boats may easily become caught within the circular motion (hydraulic) of the dam's fast-moving water. The boat and its passengers may be unable to escape. Low-head dams are particularly difficult to spot on the upstream side; and from any vantage point, they can look harmless. Remember that no matter how short a drop the dam may have, it can still be deadly.

**INFO**

- *Always portage around low-head dams, regardless of direction of approach. Exit the water well before the dam and return well after.*

- *Not all low-head dams are marked by signage or a danger buoy. Therefore, familiarize yourself with any stream or river before traveling on it.*

- *When traveling downstream, watch for a smooth horizon line. This is a subtle but telltale sign that you are approaching a low-head dam. The scenery beyond it might have the illusion of being cut off or shortened.*

## America's Waterway Watch

The U.S. Coast Guard is asking boaters to help keep America's waterways safe and secure.

The Coast Guard has developed a program called America's Waterway Watch (www.americaswaterwaywatch.org). It asks boaters to call 877-24WATCH if they notice suspicious activity or behavior on or near the water.

Things to report include:

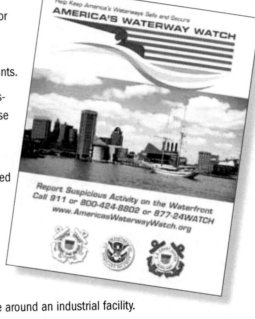

- Someone taking pictures, video, or making sketches of facilities like bridges, tunnels, ferry transport systems, fuel docks, or power plants.

- Someone asking a series of questions about access to one of these facilities.

- Someone anchoring, fishing, or diving in an area not typically used for that activity.

- Unattended vessels in unusual locations.

- Unusual transfer of personnel or cargo while underway.

- Seeing a hole in a security fence around an industrial facility.

*Do not* take matters into your own hands. Call 877-24WATCH. In cases of immediate danger to life or property, call the Coast Guard on Channel 16 VHF-FM, or dial 911 for emergencies.

## 7. ALWAYS WEAR YOUR LIFE JACKET!
*(and require the same of your passengers)*

The number one cause of on-the-water fatalities is drowning. The number one way to prevent drowning is to wear a life jacket.

The U.S. Coast Guard requires recreational vessels to have a wearable life jacket for each person on board.

All life jackets must be:

· U. S. Coast Guard-approved.

· The proper size for the intended wearer.

· In good and serviceable condition.

· Properly stowed (readily accessible).

### Children Must Wear Life Jackets

Federal regulations require that on a recreational vessel underway, children under 13 must wear an appropriate U. S. Coast Guard-approved life jacket, unless they are below decks or in an enclosed cabin. Within a state's waters, if that state has established a child lifejacket wear requirement, that state's requirement applies.

The Coast Guard recommends *all* passengers wear a life jacket at all times when the vessel is underway.

### Tips for a Proper Fit – Try It On

· Use the manufacturer's label as a guide to choosing the proper life jacket for your size and weight. It should have a comfortably snug fit.

· With all straps, zippers, and ties securely fastened, raise your arms over your head. The jacket should stay in place and not ride up.

· With your arms at your sides, have someone lift your life jacket straight up at the shoulders. If the jacket comes up more than a few inches, it is too loose.

· It is best to try on a life jacket before a boat trip.

· Life jackets designed for adults will not work for children!

## Surprisingly Comfortable

Today's life jackets are lightweight, easy to move in, and come in many sizes, styles, and shapes for every person and every sport. (There are even ones for pets!) Some examples:

**Inflatable**

for general recreational boating

**Belt Pack Inflatable**

for general recreational boating

**Vest-Type Flotation Aid**

for personal watercraft, waterskiing, and water sports

**Child Hybrid Inflatable**

for general recreational boating

**Child Life Jacket**

for general recreational boating

**Flotation Aid**

for general recreational boating

**Vest Type**

for general recreational boating

**Inflatable Fishing Vest**

for angling and hunting

**Paddling Jacket**

for paddlesports

**Offshore Vest**

for offshore boating and racing

## Key to the U.S. Aids to Navigation System (IALA-B)

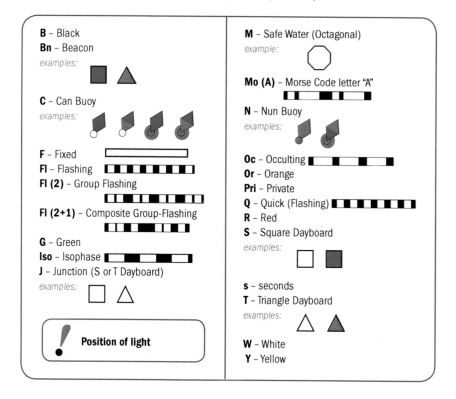

**B** – Black
**Bn** – Beacon
*examples:*

**C** – Can Buoy
*examples:*

**F** – Fixed
**Fl** – Flashing
**Fl (2)** – Group Flashing

**Fl (2+1)** – Composite Group-Flashing

**G** – Green
**Iso** – Isophase
**J** – Junction (S or T Dayboard)
*examples:*

**Position of light**

**M** – Safe Water (Octagonal)
*example:*

**Mo (A)** – Morse Code letter "A"

**N** – Nun Buoy
*examples:*

**Oc** – Occulting
**Or** – Orange
**Pri** – Private
**Q** – Quick (Flashing)
**R** – Red
**S** – Square Dayboard
*examples:*

**s** – seconds
**T** – Triangle Dayboard
*examples:*

**W** – White
**Y** – Yellow

### How to Report Aids to Navigation Discrepancies to the Coast Guard

Please report discrepancies or outages to any Aid to Navigation (GPS, DGPS, buoys, lights, dayboards, etc.) to the nearest U.S. Coast Guard station. You can do this 24 hours a day, 7 days a week via radio, telephone, fax, visiting www.navcen.uscg.gov, or by e-mailing navcen@uscg.mil. To reach the U.S. Coast Guard Navigation Center by telephone, call (703) 313-5900.

Reporting can help prevent accidents caused by such defects; you will be helping other boaters stay safe.

### All Aids to Navigation are Protected By Law

It is a criminal offense to cause any damage or hindrance to the proper operation of any Aid. Do not alter, deface, move, or destroy any Aid to Navigation. Never tie a vessel to a buoy, daybeacon, or light structure. Avoid anchoring so close to an Aid that the Aid is obstructed (hidden) from sight of another vessel. Report all intentional or unintentional collisions with navigation Aids to the U.S. Coast Guard.

# Notes